Pokémon

Pokémon Pals   6
New Pokémon Profiles Part 1   7
The Face Off!   14
Word Up!   16
Attack of the Prehistoric Pokémon   18
Me And My Shadow!   32
A Fine Art!   34
Pokémon Profiles Part 2   36
Ash-tonishing!   48
Pokémon Creator   50
Electric Shock Showdown   52
The Great Escape   64
Split Up   66
Day of the Donphan   67
Going Dotty   75
Name That Pokémon   76
Pokémon Profiles Part 3   78
Team Rocket   91
Pokémon Search   92
Word Puzzle   94
Bye, Bye, Butterfree   95

Pedigree®

Published by Pedigree Books Limited
The Old Rectory, Matford Lane, Exeter EX2 4PS
E-mail books@pedigreegroup.co.uk
Published in 2001

£6.99

POKÉMON PALS

Meet your Pokémon your friends, Ash, Misty and Brock.

Ash is a young Pokémon trainer who wants to win every battle and collect all the Pokémon and rise to the rank of a Master Trainer.

Misty is a collector who likes to catch Water Pokémon most of all.

Brock is a breeder who raises the best Pokémon and brings out their inner strength and personality.

Before you can catch a Pokémon you will need a Poké Ball to put it in. The Pokédex is full of valuable information to help you train the Pokémon.

Pokémon Update

27 FANTASTIC NEW Pokémon TO COLLECT

Read about these latest Pokémon characters and the powers they possess! Are they stronger or weaker than your current favourite Pokémon? We'll give you the low-down on each of these new Pokémon, then it's up to you to decide!

169

CROBAT™

Pokémon:	Bat
HEIGHT:	1.8m
WEIGHT:	75kg
TYPE:	Poison/Flying
ATTACKS:	Screech , Leech Life , Supersonic, Bite Confuse Ray, Wing Attack

The development of wings on its legs enables it to fly fast but also makes it tough to stop and rest. It flies so silently through the dark on its four wings that it may not be noticed even when nearby.

186

POLITOED™

Pokémon:	Frog
HEIGHT:	1.1m
WEIGHT:	33.9kg
TYPE:	Water
ATTACKS:	Water Gun, Hypnosis, Doubleslap Perish Song, Swagger

Whenever three or more of these get together, they sing in a loud voice that sounds like bellowing. If POLIWAG and POLIWHIRL hear its echoing cry, they respond by gathering from far and wide.

196

ESPEON™

Pokémon:	Sun
HEIGHT:	0.9m
WEIGHT:	26.5kg
TYPE:	Psychic
ATTACKS:	Tackle, Sand-Attack, Confusion, Quick Attack, Swift, Psybeam

By reading air currents, it can predict things such as the weather or its foe's next move.

UMBREON™

Pokémon:	Moonlight
HEIGHT:	1.0m
WEIGHT:	27kg
TYPE:	Dark
ATTACKS:	Tackle, Tail Whip, Sand-Attack, Pursuit, Quick Attack

When darkness falls, the rings on the body begin to glow, striking fear in the hearts of anyone nearby.

MISDREAVUS™

Pokémon:	Screech
HEIGHT:	0.7m
WEIGHT:	1kg
TYPE:	Ghost
ATTACKS:	Spite, Confuse Ray, Mean Look, Psybeam, Pain Split, Perish Song

It loves to bite and yank people's hair from behind without warning, just to see their shocked reactions.

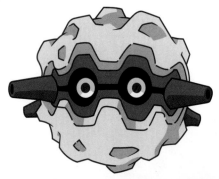

FORRETRESS™

Pokémon:	Bagworm
HEIGHT:	1.2m
WEIGHT:	125.8kg
TYPE:	Bug/Steel
ATTACKS:	Tackle, Protect, Self-destruct, Rapid Spin, Bide, Explosion, Spikes

It remains immovably rooted to its tree. It scatters pieces of its hard shell to drive its enemies away.

DUNSPARCE™

Pokémon:	Land Snake
HEIGHT:	1.5m
WEIGHT:	14kg
TYPE:	Normal
ATTACKS:	Defense Curl, Glare, Spite, Pursuit, Screech, Take Down

If spotted, it escapes by burrowing with its tail. It can float just slightly using its wings.

211

QWILFISH™

Pokémon:	Balloon
HEIGHT:	0.5m
WEIGHT:	3.9kg
TYPE:	Water/Poison
ATTACKS:	Tackle, Poison Sting, Harden, Minimize, Water Gun, Pin Missile

The small spikes covering its body developed from scales. They inject a toxin that causes fainting.

212

SCIZOR™

Pokémon:	Scissors
HEIGHT:	1.8m
WEIGHT:	118kg
TYPE:	Bug/Steel
ATTACKS:	Quick Attack, Leer, Focus Energy, Pursuit, False Swipe, Agility, Metal Claw, Slash, Swords Dance

Its wings are not used for flying. They are flapped at high speed to adjust its body temperature.

215

SNEASEL™

Pokémon:	Sharp Claw
HEIGHT:	0.9m
WEIGHT:	28kg
TYPE:	Dark/Ice
ATTACKS:	Quick Attack, Screech, Faint Attack, Fury Swipes, Agility, Slash, Beat Up

Vicious in nature, it drives PIDGEY from their nests and feasts on the eggs that are left behind.

218

SLUGMA™

Pokémon:	Lava
HEIGHT:	0.7m
WEIGHT:	35kg
TYPE:	Fire
ATTACKS:	Smog, Ember, Rock Throw, Harden, Amnesia, Flamethrower, Rock Slide

A common sight in volcanic areas, it slowly slithers around in a constant search for warm places.

(219)

MAGCARGO™

Pokémon:	Lava
HEIGHT:	0.8m
WEIGHT:	55kg
TYPE:	Fire/Rock
ATTACKS:	Smog, Ember, Rock Throw, Harden, Amnesia, Flamethrower

Its brittle shell occasionally spouts intense flames that circulate throughout its body.

(222)

CORSOLA™

Pokémon:	Coral
HEIGHT:	0.6m
WEIGHT:	5kg
TYPE:	Water/Rock
ATTACKS:	Tackle, Harden, Bubble, Recover, Bubblebeam, Spike Cannon

In a south sea nation, the people live in communities that are built on groups of these POKéMON.

(223)

REMORAID™

Pokémon:	Jet
HEIGHT:	0.6m
WEIGHT:	12kg
TYPE:	Water
ATTACKS:	Water Gun, Lock-On, Aurora Beam, Psybeam, Bubblebeam

Using its dorsal fin as a suction pad, it clings to a MANTINE's underside to scavenge for leftovers.

(224)

OCTILLERY™

Pokémon:	Jet
HEIGHT:	0.9m
WEIGHT:	28.5kg
TYPE:	Water
ATTACKS:	Water Gun, Constrict, Aurora Beam, Psybeam, Bubblebeam

It instinctively sneaks into rocky holes. If it gets sleepy, it steals the nest of a fellow OCTILLERY.

225

DELIBIRD™

Pokémon:	Delivery
HEIGHT:	0.9m
WEIGHT:	16kg
TYPE:	Ice/Flying
ATTACKS:	Present, Fly

It nests at the edge of sharp cliffs. It spends all day carrying food to its awaiting chicks. It carries food all day long. There are tales about lost people who were saved by the food it had.

227

SKARMORY™

Pokémon:	Armor Bird
HEIGHT:	1.7m
WEIGHT:	50.5kg
TYPE:	Steel/Flying
ATTACKS:	Leer, Peck, Sand-Attack, Swift, Agility, Fury Attack, Steel Wing

After nesting in bramble bushes, the wings of its chicks grow hard from scratches by thorns.

228

HOUNDOUR™

Pokémon:	Dark
HEIGHT:	0.6m
WEIGHT:	10.8kg
TYPE:	Dark/Fire
ATTACKS:	Leer, Ember, Roar, Smog, Bite, Faint Attack, Flamethrower, Crunch

To corner prey, they check each other's location using barks that only they can understand.

229

HOUNDOOM™

Pokémon:	Dark
HEIGHT:	1.4m
WEIGHT:	35kg
TYPE:	Dark/Fire
ATTACKS:	Leer, Ember, Roar, Smog, Bite, Faint Attack, Flamethrower, Crunch

Upon hearing its eerie howls, other POKéMON get the shivers and head straight back to their nests.

KINGDRA™

Pokémon:	Dragon
HEIGHT:	1.8m
WEIGHT:	152kg
TYPE:	Water/Dragon
ATTACKS:	Bubble, Smokescreen, Leer, Water Gun, Twister, Agility

It sleeps deep on the ocean floor to build its energy. It is said to cause tornadoes as it wakes.

PORYGON2™

Pokémon:	Virtual
HEIGHT:	0.6m
WEIGHT:	32.5kg
TYPE:	Normal
ATTACKS:	Tackle, Conversion, Agility, Psybeam, Recover, Defense Curl

Further research enhanced its abilities. Sometimes, it may exhibit motions that were not programmed.

TYROGUE™

Pokémon:	Scuffle
HEIGHT:	0.7m
WEIGHT:	21kg
TYPE:	Fighting
ATTACKS:	Tackle, Strength

Even though it is small, it can't be ignored because it will slug any handy target without warning.

SMOOCHUM™

Pokémon:	Kiss
HEIGHT:	0.4m
WEIGHT:	6kg
TYPE:	Ice/Psychic
ATTACKS:	Pound, Lick, Sweet Kiss, Powder Snow, Confusion, Sing, Mean Look

It always rocks its head slowly backwards and forwards as if it is trying to kiss someone.

240

MAGBY™

Pokémon:	Live Coal
HEIGHT:	0.7m
WEIGHT:	21.4kg
TYPE:	Fire
ATTACKS:	Ember, Leer, Smog, Fire Punch, Smokescreen, Sunny Day

It is found in volcanic craters. Its body temp. is over 1100 degrees, so don't underestimate it.

246

LARVITAR™

Pokémon:	Rock Skin
HEIGHT:	0.6m
WEIGHT:	72kg
TYPE:	Rock/Ground
ATTACKS:	Bite, Leer, Sandstorm, Screech, Rock Slide, Thrash, Scary Face, Crunch

It is born deep underground. It can't emerge until it has entirely consumed the soil around it.

247

PUPITAR™

Pokémon:	Hard Shell
HEIGHT:	1.2m
WEIGHT:	152kg
TYPE:	Rock/Ground
ATTACKS:	Bite, Leer, Sandstorm, Screech, Rock Slide, Thrash, Scary Face, Crunch

Even sealed in its shell, it can move freely. Hard and fast, it has outstanding destructive power.

248

TYRANITAR™

Pokémon:	Armor
HEIGHT:	2.0m
WEIGHT:	202kg
TYPE:	Rock/Dark
ATTACKS:	Bite, Leer, Sandstorm, Screech, Rock Slide, Thrash, Scary Face, Crunch

Extremely strong, it can change the landscape. It has an insolent nature that makes it not care about others.

Pokémon THE FACE-OFF!

Noughts & Crosses games, Pokémon Style!

Hi, guys! As you know, to become a Pokémon Master, you must train your Pokémon in the art of battle, so they can learn valuable experience and learn new techniques!

If you want to be as good as me, practise as much as you can! Challenge a friend to a Pokémon competition. Choose your six favourite Pokémon, for their strength, speed and agility. Flip a coin to see who starts, then you each in turn put the first letter of your chosen Pokémon into one of the squares of the six grids on the following pages.

You can jump from grid to grid, and change your Pokémon whenever you want, remembering to shout "I choose you" before you do so.

The aim of the competition is to be the first to get three of your Pokémon in a straight line, either across, down or diagonally. The Pokémon trainer who wins the most grids wins the competition!

Pokémon WORD UP!

Can you help Ash, Misty and Brock find the names of these 16 Pokémon hidden in this word search? The names can be found up, down, across, diagonally, and even back-to-front!

WARTORTLE

RATICATE

BULBASAUR

TENTACOOL

CHARMANDER

PIKACHU

ZUBAT

SQUIRTLE

PARAS   **MACHAMP**   **MEOWTH**   **ONIX**

BUTTERFREE   **CATERPIE**   **PSYDUCK**   **GLOOM**

```
C W H T W O E M S X S A R A P
A T E N T A C O O L K T B F S
T S C R S X N F E G L O O M I
E A A E W I U O P R D Q E X W
R F T D X H J S Q U I R T L E
P A I N C C S Q V A W A I I B
I A S A M J U X W S I T G K G
E O K M I H U F T A G I M C I
W I S R C E R T Y B S C H U P
P I W A R T O R T L E A W D L
W I Y H O A Z B U U M T N Y O
P D T C R Y P U U B T E F S L
P M A H C A M A W Z I S X P J
Z U B A T E E R F R E T T U B
```

Attack of the Prehistoric Pokémon

One day, Ash, Pikachu, Misty and Brock found themselves in beautiful Grandpa Canyon. They were about to discover that this natural wonder held an ancient secret.

The friends weren't alone. Hundreds of people were heading into the canyon.

"I wonder what everyone is doing with those picks and shovels," said Ash.

The friends soon found out that a "Great Fossil Rush" was on.

"Wow!" said Ash. "Look at all those people digging!"
Brock didn't seem impressed. "All these people are digging, but nobody's found any fossils yet," he remarked. "I wonder if this 'Great Fossil Rush' is for real."
"Sure it is!" said Ash, who secretly wished he were digging, too.
Meanwhile, not far from Ash and his friends, Meowth had been waiting for the rest of Team Rocket to show up.

"You're late," Meowth said to Jessie and James. "Did you two clowns plant the dynamite yet?"
"We'll blast Grandpa Canyon to smithereens and scoop up all those Poké-fossils!" said James.
Team Rocket should have whispered, because Ash, Misty and Brock overheard their evil plan.
"Did you hear that – they're gonna blow up this whole canyon!" exclaimed Brock.
"Pikachu and I will stop them!" said Ash. "Spread the word to run for it – there's no time to lose!"

Meowth lit the fuse that led to a huge keg of dynamite. "Pretty soon we'll have all the Pokémon fossils to ourselves!" Meowth exclaimed. Ash and Pikachu rushed up to Team Rocket.

"Stop!" cried Ash. "Hold it there!"

21

"It's that pest again!" said James.
"Always messing up our plans!" added Jessie.
"But this time you're too late!" said Meowth. "The fuse is already lit!"

Ash knew it was now or never.
"Gotta stop them!" he said, quicky pulling out a Poké Ball.
"Squirtle!" he called. "I choose you! There's no time to lose!
Squirtle, squirt out the fuse!"

"You can do it, Squirtle!" coached Ash, as his Pokémon squirted water at the flame. But Team Rocket wasn't about to give up so easily.
"Arbok, Go!" cried Jessie.
"Weezing!" ordered James.
"Keep that fuse lit!"
Team Rocket, Weezing and Arbok chased Ash and Squirtle down into the canyon. Someone tripped and soon everyone was rolling together, pell-mell, faster and faster into the canyon. Just as they crashed to a stop, the flame reached the keg – and the dynamite exploded!

The entire group fell down, down – through a deep hole created by the explosion! They all landed with a thud.
"Where are we?" asked James, as everyone looked around at their strange new surroundings.

"This is a cave!" exclaimed Meowth. "The dynamite must 'a blown a hole in the roof, and we fell in! We must be buried deep under the Earth's crust!"

"If you hadn't tried to put out that fuse, we never would've fallen down here!" Jessie yelled at Ash.

"Hey," shouted Ash. "You're the crooks who planted all that dynamite up there!"

That's when Meowth pointed upward to show that the roof of the cave was blocked. They were trapped!

"Chu ... Pi!" said Pikachu.

The group turned to see ... lots of glowing red eyes! Slowly, some fierce-looking, primitive creatures revealed themselves. Ash's hand shook as he pulled

out his Pokédex for information. "Omanyte ...and Omastar. Kabuto ... and Kabutops," reported the mechanical voice of Dexter. "It is believed these Pokémon became extinct tens of thousands of years ago ... none of these Pokémon have ever been seen alive.

"They look like they just woke up," observed Jessie.

"Maybe these Pokémon weren't fossilised, but were just sleeping! The dynamite must have woken them up after thousands of years!" Suddenly, the ancient Pokémon ran away.

Meanwhile, above ground, Misty and Brock were frantic. They sent Officer Jenny to get help. "Hang on, Ash!" cried Misty, and she, Brock, Squirtle and Geodude pulled rocks away from the opening.

The group soon realised why the prehistoric Pokémon had fled. Watching all the action from a high rock was a huge flying creature with claws and fangs. Once again, Ash checked the Pokédex for information.

"Aerodactyl," said Dexter. "An extinct flying Pokémon. Its fangs suggest that it was a carnivore. Its sharp claws were used to capture prey."

"What's a carnivore?" asked Ash.

"That means it thinks we're dinner!" cried James.

Just then, Aerodactyl swooped down over the group – and grabbed Ash! As the creature took off with Ash in its claws, quick-thinking Pikachu and Charmeleon grabbed on to it's tail. Aerodactyl flew up to the top of the cave, and crashed right through the blocked-in roof. That's when Pikachu and Charmeleon lost hold, and fell near Misty and Brock.

Aerodactyl landed on a rock. It kept Ash in its big claws.
"Somebody get me down from here!" called Ash to his friends below.

Meanwhile, a Pokémon named Jigglypuff had been hanging around the area, trying to get attention. It wanted to sing for everybody. When Misty saw it, she got an idea.
"Jigglypuff!" said Misty. "If you help us out now, later we'll listen to your song as much as you want." Jigglypuff happily agreed. But before Jigglypuff had a chance to sing ...

Charmeleon evolved into Charizard!
"Whoa! Charizard!" shouted Ash.
He couldn't believe his little Pokémon
was changing.
When Aerodactyl saw Charizard, it
knew it had met its match ... so it took
off with Ash still in its claws.

Charizard followed Aerodactyl into the
air with its mighty wings. It was ready
for battle!

29

As Charizard chased Aerodactyl, it breathed a ball of fire on the prehistoric Pokémon. The flame came dangerously close to Ash. During the air battle, Misty turned to Jigglypuff and said, "Please, Jigglypuff! Sing your slumber song now!"

Jigglypuff sang its hypnotic slumber song, which made everyone, including Aerodactyl, very sleepy. Aerodactyl yawned, then fell asleep in mid-air. Its claws loosened their grip on Ash, who began to fall. But Charizard flew over to catch him, and then placed him gently on the ground ... near a strange-looking object.

Meanwhile, Aerodactyl plunged down through the opening to the cave and landed with a crash. Team Rocket was still down there ... hoping not to become extinct!

All the diggers began to wake up, wondering if what they'd seen had been a dream.

"Jigglypuff and Charizard really saved the day this time!" said Ash, as he and his friends left the site.

They left with a souvenir of their adventure ... the mysterious egg.

What was inside? Only time would tell!

POKÉMON

Silhouette Game

ME AND MY SHADOW!

Those rotten Team Rocket have developed a weapon that turns Pokémon into a shadow of their former selves. Can you match up the Pokémon with their shadows?

GENGAR

BEEDRILL

IGGLYBUFF

DODRIO

PARASECT

RAPIDASH

TOGETIC

AZUMARILL

RAICHU

NINETALES

POKÉMON
A FINE ART!

Hey, Pokémon fans! Using this picture of Ash, Pikachu and Chikorita carefully colour the picture opposite.

POKÉMON

PROFILES

01

BULBASAUR™
Seed Pokémon

PRONUNCIATION:	BUL-buh-saur
TYPE:	Grass/Poison
HEIGHT:	0.7m WEIGHT: 6.9kg
ATTACKS:	Tackle, Growl
STRONG AGAINST:	Grass, Water, Ground, Rock
WEAK AGAINST:	Grass, Bug, Fire, Fighting, Flying, Poison, Ground, Rock, Ghost, Dark, Dragon, Steel
EVOLUTION:	Bulbasaur =>Ivysaur => Venusaur

02

IVYSAUR™
Seed Pokémon

PRONUNCIATION:	EYE-vee-saur
TYPE:	Grass/Poison
HEIGHT:	1.0m WEIGHT: 13kg
ATTACKS:	Tackle, Growl, Leech Seed, Vine Whip
STRONG AGAINST:	Grass, Water, Ground, Rock
WEAK AGAINST:	Grass, Bug, Fire, Fighting, Flying, Poison, Ground, Rock, Ghost, Dark, Dragon, Steel
EVOLUTION:	Bulbasaur =>Ivysaur => Venusaur

03

VENUSAUR™
Seed Pokémon

PRONUNCIATION:	VEE-nuh-saur
TYPE:	Grass/Poison
HEIGHT:	2.0m WEIGHT: 100kg
ATTACKS:	Tackle, Growl, Leech Seed, Vine Whip, Poisonpowder, Razor Leaf
STRONG AGAINST:	Grass, Water, Ground, Rock
WEAK AGAINST:	Grass, Bug, Fire, Fighting, Flying, Poison, Ground, Rock, Ghost, Dark, Dragon, Steel
EVOLUTION:	Bulbasaur =>Ivysaur => Venusaur

04

CHARMANDER™
Lizard Pokémon

PRONUNCIATION:	CHAR-man-der
TYPE:	Fire
HEIGHT:	0.6m WEIGHT: 8.5kg
ATTACKS:	Scratch, Growl
STRONG AGAINST:	Grass, Ice, Bug, Steel
WEAK AGAINST:	Fire, Water, Rock, Dragon
EVOLUTION:	Charmander=>Charmeleon =>Charizard

05

CHARMELEON™
Flame Pokémon

PRONUNCIATION:	char-MEAL-ee-ehn
TYPE:	Fire
HEIGHT:	1.1m WEIGHT: 19kg
ATTACKS:	Scratch, Growl, Ember
STRONG AGAINST:	Grass, Ice, Bug, Steel
WEAK AGAINST:	Fire, Water, Rock, Dragon
EVOLUTION:	Charmander=>Charmeleon =>Charizard

06

CHARIZARD™
Flame Pokémon

PRONUNCIATION:	CHAR-izard
TYPE:	Fire/Flying
HEIGHT:	1.7m WEIGHT: 90.5kg
ATTACKS:	Scratch, Growl, Ember, Leer
STRONG AGAINST:	Grass, Fighting, Bug, Ice, Steel
WEAK AGAINST:	Electric, Fire, Rock, Water, Dragon
EVOLUTION:	Charmander=>Charmeleon =>Charizard

07

SQUIRTLE™
Tinyturtle Pokémon

PRONUNCIATION:	SKWUR-tull
TYPE:	Water
HEIGHT:	0.5m WEIGHT: 9kg
ATTACKS:	Tackle, Tail Whip
STRONG AGAINST:	Fire, Ground, Rock
WEAK AGAINST:	Water, Grass, Dragon
EVOLUTION:	Squirtle=>Wartortle=> Blastoise

08 WARTORTLE™
Turtle Pokémon
PRONUNCIATION:	WAR-tor-tull
TYPE:	Water
HEIGHT:	1m WEIGHT: 22.5kg
ATTACKS:	Tackle, Tail Whip, Bubble
STRONG AGAINST:	Fire, Ground, Rock
WEAK AGAINST:	Water, Grass, Dragon
EVOLUTION:	Squirtle=>Wartortle=> Blastoise

09 BLASTOISE™
Shellfish Pokémon
PRONUNCIATION:	BLAST-oys
TYPE:	Water
HEIGHT:	1.6m WEIGHT: 85.5kg
ATTACKS:	Tackle, Tail Whip, Bubble, Water Gun
STRONG AGAINST:	Fire, Ground, Rock
WEAK AGAINST:	Water, Grass, Dragon
EVOLUTION:	Squirtle=>Wartortle=> Blastoise

10 CATERPIE™
Worm Pokémon
PRONUNCIATION:	CAT-er-pee
TYPE:	Bug
HEIGHT:	0.3m WEIGHT: 2.9kg
ATTACKS:	Tackle, String Shot
STRONG AGAINST:	Grass, Psychic, Dark
WEAK AGAINST:	Ghost, Flying, Fighting, Fire, Steel
EVOLUTION:	Caterpie=>Metapod=> Butterfree

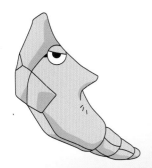

11 METAPOD™
Cocoon Pokémon
PRONUNCIATION:	MET-uh-pod
TYPE:	Bug
HEIGHT:	0.7m WEIGHT: 99kg
ATTACKS:	Harden
STRONG AGAINST:	Grass, Psychic, Dark
WEAK AGAINST:	Ghost, Flying, Fighting, Fire, Steel
EVOLUTION:	Caterpie=>Metapod=> Butterfree

12 BUTTERFREE™
Butterfly Pokémon
PRONUNCIATION:	BUT-er-free
TYPE:	Bug/Flying
HEIGHT:	1.1m WEIGHT: 32kg
ATTACKS:	Poisonpowder, Confusion
STRONG AGAINST:	Grass, Fighting, Bug, Psychic, Dark
WEAK AGAINST:	Electric, Fire, Fighting, Flying, Ghost, Rock, Steel
EVOLUTION:	Caterpie=>Metapod=> Butterfree

13 WEEDLE™
Hairy Bug Pokémon
PRONUNCIATION:	WEE-dull
TYPE:	Bug/Poison
HEIGHT:	0.3m WEIGHT: 3.2kg
ATTACKS:	Poison Sting, String Shot
STRONG AGAINST:	Grass, Psychic, Dark
WEAK AGAINST:	Fire, Fighting, Flying, Ground, Rock, Ghost, Steel
EVOLUTION:	Weedle=>Kakuna=> Beedrill

14 KAKUNA™
Cocoon Pokémon
PRONUNCIATION:	ka-KOO-nuh
TYPE:	Bug/Poison
HEIGHT:	0.6m WEIGHT: 10kg
ATTACKS:	Harden
STRONG AGAINST:	Grass, Psychic, Dark
WEAK AGAINST:	Fire, Fighting, Flying, Ground, Rock, Ghost, Steel
EVOLUTION:	Weedle=>Kakuna=> Beedrill

15 BEEDRILL™
Poison Bee Pokémon
PRONUNCIATION:	BEE-drill
TYPE:	Bug/Poison
HEIGHT:	1.0m WEIGHT: 29.5kg
ATTACKS:	Fury Attack, Focus Energy
STRONG AGAINST:	Grass, Psychic, Dark
WEAK AGAINST:	Fire, Fighting, Flying, Ground, Rock, Ghost, Steel
EVOLUTION:	Weedle=>Kakuna=> Beedrill

16 PIDGEY™
Tiny Bird Pokémon
PRONUNCIATION:	PID-jee
TYPE:	Normal/Flying
HEIGHT:	0.3m WEIGHT: 1.8kg
ATTACKS:	Gust
STRONG AGAINST:	Grass, Fighting, Bug
WEAK AGAINST:	Electric, Rock, Steel
EVOLUTION:	Pidgey=>Pidgeotto=> Pidgeot

PIDGEOTTO™
Bird Pokémon
PRONUNCIATION: pid-JYO-toe
TYPE: Normal/Flying
HEIGHT: 1.1m **WEIGHT:** 30kg
ATTACKS: Gust, Sand-Attack, Quick Attack
STRONG AGAINST: Grass, Fighting, Bug
WEAK AGAINST: Electric, Rock, Steel
EVOLUTION: Pidgey=>Pidgeotto=> Pidgeot

PIDGEOT™
Bird Pokémon
PRONUNCIATION: PID-jit
TYPE: Normal/Flying
HEIGHT: 1.5m **WEIGHT:** 39.5kg
ATTACKS: Gust, Sand-Attack, Quick Attack , Whirlwind, Wing Attack
STRONG AGAINST: Grass, Fighting, Bug
WEAK AGAINST: Electric, Rock, Steel
EVOLUTION: Pidgey=>Pidgeotto=> Pidgeot

RATTATA™
Rat Pokémon
PRONUNCIATION: ruh-TA-tah
TYPE: Normal
HEIGHT: 0.3m **WEIGHT:** 3.5kg
ATTACKS: Tackle, Tail Whip
STRONG AGAINST: None
WEAK AGAINST: Rock, Steel
EVOLUTION: Rattata=>Raticate

RATICATE™
Rat Pokémon
PRONUNCIATION: RAT-i-kate
TYPE: Normal
HEIGHT: 0.7m **WEIGHT:** 18.5kg
ATTACKS: Tackle, Tail Whip, Quick Attack
STRONG AGAINST: None
WEAK AGAINST: Rock, Steel
EVOLUTION: Rattata=>Raticate

SPEAROW™
Tiny Bird Pokémon
PRONUNCIATION: SPEER-oh
TYPE: Normal/Flying
HEIGHT: 0.3m **WEIGHT:** 2kg
ATTACKS: Peck, Growl
STRONG AGAINST: Grass, Fighting, Bug
WEAK AGAINST: Electric, Rock, Steel
EVOLUTION: Spearow=>Fearow

FEAROW™
Beak Pokémon
PRONUNCIATION: FEER-oh
TYPE: Normal/Flying
HEIGHT: 1.2m **WEIGHT:** 38kg
ATTACKS: Peck, Growl, Leer, Fury Attack
STRONG AGAINST: Grass, Fighting, Bug
WEAK AGAINST: Electric, Rock, Steel
EVOLUTION: Spearow=>Fearow

EKANS™
Snake Pokémon
PRONUNCIATION: ECK-uhns
TYPE: Poison
HEIGHT: 2.0m **WEIGHT:** 6.9kg
ATTACKS: Wrap, Leer
STRONG AGAINST: Grass
WEAK AGAINST: Poison, Ground, Rock, Ghost
EVOLUTION: Ekans=>Arbok

ARBOK™
Cobra Pokémon
PRONUNCIATION: AR-bock
TYPE: Poison
HEIGHT: 3.5m **WEIGHT:** 65kg
ATTACKS: Wrap, Leer, Poison Sting
STRONG AGAINST: Grass
WEAK AGAINST: Poison, Ground, Rock, Ghost
EVOLUTION: Ekans=>Arbok

PIKACHU™
Mouse Pokémon
PRONUNCIATION: PEEK-uh-chew
TYPE: Electric
HEIGHT: 0.4m **WEIGHT:** 6kg
ATTACKS: Thundershock, Growl
STRONG AGAINST: Water, Flying
WEAK AGAINST: Electric, Grass, Dragon
EVOLUTION: Pichu=>Pikachu=>Raichu

26

RAICHU™
Mouse Pokémon

PRONUNCIATION:	RYE-chew
TYPE:	Electric
HEIGHT:	0.8m WEIGHT: 30kg
ATTACKS:	Thundershock
STRONG AGAINST:	Water, Flying
WEAK AGAINST:	Electric, Grass, Dragon
EVOLUTION:	Pichu=>Pikachu=>Raichu

27

SANDSHREW™
Mouse Pokémon

PRONUNCIATION:	SAND-shroo
TYPE:	Ground
HEIGHT:	0.6m WEIGHT: 12kg
ATTACKS:	Scratch
STRONG AGAINST:	Electric, Fire, Poison, Rock, Steel
WEAK AGAINST:	Grass, Bug
EVOLUTION:	Sandshrew=>Sandslash

28

SANDSLASH™
Mouse Pokémon

PRONUNCIATION:	SAND-slash
TYPE:	Ground
HEIGHT:	1.0m WEIGHT: 29.5kg
ATTACKS:	Scratch, Sand-Attack, Slash
STRONG AGAINST:	Electric, Fire, Poison, Rock, Steel
WEAK AGAINST:	Grass, Bug
EVOLUTION:	Sandshrew=>Sandslash

29

NIDORAN♀™
Poison Pin Pokémon

PRONUNCIATION:	nee-door-ANN
TYPE:	Poison
HEIGHT:	0.4m WEIGHT: 7kg
ATTACKS:	Growl, Tackle
STRONG AGAINST:	Grass
WEAK AGAINST:	Poison, Ground, Rock, Ghost
EVOLUTION:	Nidoran=>Nidorina=> Nidoqueen

30

NIDORINA™
Poison Pin Pokémon

PRONUNCIATION:	nee-door-EE-nuh
TYPE:	Poison
HEIGHT:	0.8m WEIGHT: 20kg
ATTACKS:	Growl, Tackle, Scratch
STRONG AGAINST:	Grass
WEAK AGAINST:	Poison, Ground, Rock, Ghost
EVOLUTION:	Nidoran=>Nidorina=> Nidoqueen

31

NIDOQUEEN™
Drill Pokémon

PRONUNCIATION:	nee-doe-QUEEN
TYPE:	Poison/Ground
HEIGHT:	1.3m WEIGHT: 60kg
ATTACKS:	Tackle, Scratch, Tail Whip
STRONG AGAINST:	Grass, Fire, Electric, Poison, Rock, Steel
WEAK AGAINST:	Grass, Bug, Poison, Ground, Rock, Ghost
EVOLUTION:	Nidoran=>Nidorina=> Nidoqueen

32

NIDORAN♂™
Poison Pin Pokémon

PRONUNCIATION:	nee-door-ANN
TYPE:	Poison
HEIGHT:	0.5m WEIGHT: 9kg
ATTACKS:	Leer, Tackle
STRONG AGAINST:	Grass
WEAK AGAINST:	Poison, Ground, Rock, Ghost
EVOLUTION:	Nidoran=>Nidorino=> Nidoking

33

NIDORINO™
Poison Pin Pokémon

PRONUNCIATION:	nee-door-ee-no
TYPE:	Poison
HEIGHT:	0.9m WEIGHT: 19.5kg
ATTACKS:	Leer, Tackle, Horn Attack
STRONG AGAINST:	Grass
WEAK AGAINST:	Poison, Ground, Rock, Ghost
EVOLUTION:	Nidoran=>Nidorino=> Nidoking

34

NIDOKING™
Drill Pokémon

PRONUNCIATION:	nee-doe-KING
TYPE:	Poison/Ground
HEIGHT:	1.4m WEIGHT: 62kg
STRONG AGAINST:	Grass, Fire, Electric, Poison, Rock, Steel
WEAK AGAINST:	Grass, Bug, Poison, Ground, Rock, Ghost
EVOLUTION:	Nidoran=>Nidorino=> Nidoking

CLEFAIRY™
Fairy Pokémon

PRONUNCIATION: cluh-FAIR-ee
TYPE: Normal
HEIGHT: 0.6m WEIGHT: 7.5kg
ATTACKS: Pound, Growl
STRONG AGAINST: None
WEAK AGAINST: Rock, Steel
EVOLUTION: Cleffa=>Clefairy=>
Clefable

CLEFABLE™
Fairy Pokémon

PRONUNCIATION: cluh-FAY-bull
TYPE: Normal
HEIGHT: 1.3m WEIGHT: 40kg
ATTACKS: Sing, Doublesplat,
Metronome
STRONG AGAINST: None
WEAK AGAINST: Rock, Steel
EVOLUTION: Cleffa=>Clefairy=>
Clefable

VULPIX™
Fox Pokémon

PRONUNCIATION: VULL-picks
TYPE: Fire
HEIGHT: 0.6m WEIGHT: 9.9kg
ATTACKS: Ember, Tail Whip
STRONG AGAINST: Grass, Ice, Bug, Steel
WEAK AGAINST: Fire, Water, Rock, Dragon
EVOLUTION: Vulpix=>Ninetales

NINETALES™
Fox Pokémon

PRONUNCIATION: NINE-tails
TYPE: Fire
HEIGHT: 1.1m WEIGHT: 19.9kg
ATTACKS: Ember, Quick Attack
STRONG AGAINST: Grass, Ice, Bug, Steel
WEAK AGAINST: Fire, Water, Rock, Dragon
EVOLUTION: Vulpix=>Ninetales

JIGGLYPUFF™
Balloon Pokémon

PRONUNCIATION: jig-lee-PUFF
TYPE: Normal
HEIGHT: 0.5m WEIGHT: 5.5kg
ATTACKS: Sing
STRONG AGAINST: None
WEAK AGAINST: Rock, Steel
EVOLUTION: Igglybuff=>Jigglypuff=>
Wigglytuff

WIGGLYTUFF™
Balloon Pokémon

PRONUNCIATION: wig-lee-TUFF
TYPE: Normal
HEIGHT: 1.0m WEIGHT: 12kg
ATTACKS: Sing, Disable, Defence
Curl, Doubleslap
STRONG AGAINST: None
WEAK AGAINST: Rock, Steel
EVOLUTION: Igglybuff=>Jigglypuff=>
Wigglytuff

ZUBAT™
Bat Pokémon

PRONUNCIATION: ZOO-bat
TYPE: Poison/Flying
HEIGHT: 0.8m WEIGHT: 7.5kg
ATTACKS: Leech Life
STRONG AGAINST: Grass, Fighting, Bug
WEAK AGAINST: Poison, Ground, Electric
Rock, Ghost
EVOLUTION: Zubat=>Golbat

GOLBAT™
Bat Pokémon

PRONUNCIATION: GOAL-bat
TYPE: Poison/Flying
HEIGHT: 1.6m WEIGHT: 55kg
ATTACKS: Leech Life
STRONG AGAINST: Grass, Fighting, Bug
WEAK AGAINST: Poison, Ground, Electric
Rock, Ghost
EVOLUTION: Zubat=>Golbat

ODDISH™
Weed Pokémon

PRONUNCIATION: ODD-ish
TYPE: Grass/Poison
HEIGHT: 0.5m WEIGHT: 5.4kg
ATTACKS: Absorb
STRONG AGAINST: Grass, Water, Ground, Rock
WEAK AGAINST: Grass, Bug, Fire, Fighting,
Flying, Poison, Ground, Rock, Ghost, Dark,
Dragon, Steel
EVOLUTION: Oddish=>Gloom=>Vileplume
Oddish=>Gloom=>Bellossom

GLOOM™
Weed Pokémon
PRONUNCIATION: gloom
TYPE: Grass/Poison
HEIGHT: 0.8m WEIGHT: 8.6kg
ATTACKS: Absorb, Poisonpowder, Stun Spore, Sleep Powder
STRONG AGAINST: Grass, Water, Ground, Rock
WEAK AGAINST: Grass, Bug, Fire, Fighting, Flying, Poison, Ground, Rock, Ghost, Dark, Dragon, Steel
EVOLUTION: Oddish=>Gloom=>Vileplume
Oddish=>Gloom=>Bellossom

VILEPLUME™
Flower Pokémon
PRONUNCIATION: VILE-ploom
TYPE: Grass/Poison
HEIGHT: 1.2m WEIGHT: 18.6kg
ATTACKS: Poisonpowder, Stun Spore, Sleep Powder
STRONG AGAINST: Grass, Water, Ground, Rock
WEAK AGAINST: Grass, Bug, Fire, Fighting, Flying, Poison, Ground, Rock, Ghost, Dark, Dragon, Steel
EVOLUTION: Oddish=>Gloom=> Vileplume

PARAS™
Mushroom Pokémon
PRONUNCIATION: PAR-iss
TYPE: Bug/Grass
HEIGHT: 0.3m WEIGHT: 5.4kg
ATTACKS: Scratch
STRONG AGAINST: Water, Ground, Rock, Grass, Psychic, Dark
WEAK AGAINST: Fire, Grass, Poison, Flying, Bug, Dragon, Steel, Fighting, Ghost
EVOLUTION: Paras=>Parasect

PARASECT™
Mushroom Pokémon
PRONUNCIATION: PAR-i-sect
TYPE: Bug/Grass
HEIGHT: 1.0m WEIGHT: 29.5kg
ATTACKS: Scratch
STRONG AGAINST: Water, Ground, Rock, Grass, Psychic, Dark
WEAK AGAINST: Fire, Grass, Poison, Flying, Bug, Dragon, Steel, Fighting, Ghost
EVOLUTION: Paras=>Parasect

VENONAT™
Insect Pokémon
PRONUNCIATION: VENN-oh-nat
TYPE: Bug/Poison
HEIGHT: 1.0m WEIGHT: 30kg
ATTACKS: Tackle, Disable
STRONG AGAINST: Grass, Psychic, Dark
WEAK AGAINST: Fire, Fighting, Flying, Ground, Rock, Ghost, Steel
EVOLUTION: Venonat=>Venomoth

VENONAT™
Poisonmoth Pokémon
PRONUNCIATION: VENN-oh-moth
TYPE: Bug/Poison
HEIGHT: 1.5m WEIGHT: 12.5kg
ATTACKS: Tackle, Disable, Poisonpowder, Leech Life, Stun Spore
STRONG AGAINST: Grass, Psychic, Dark
WEAK AGAINST: Fire, Fighting, Flying, Ground, Rock, Ghost, Steel
EVOLUTION: Venonat=>Venomoth

DIGLETT™
Mole Pokémon
PRONUNCIATION: DIG-lit
TYPE: Ground
HEIGHT: 0.2m WEIGHT: 0.8kg
ATTACKS: Scratch
STRONG AGAINST: Electric, Fire, Poison, Rock, Steel
WEAK AGAINST: Grass, Bug
EVOLUTION: Diglett=>Dugtrio

DUGTRIO™
Mole Pokémon
PRONUNCIATION: dug–TREE-oh
TYPE: Ground
HEIGHT: 0.7m WEIGHT: 33.3kg
ATTACKS: Scratch, Growl, Dig, Sand-Attack
STRONG AGAINST: Electric, Fire, Poison, Rock, Steel
WEAK AGAINST: Grass, Bug
EVOLUTION: Diglett=>Dugtrio

MEOWTH™
Scratchcat Pokémon
PRONUNCIATION: me-OUTH
TYPE: Normal
HEIGHT: 0.4m WEIGHT: 4.2kg
ATTACKS: Scratch, Growl
STRONG AGAINST: None
WEAK AGAINST: Rock, Steel
EVOLUTION: Meowth=>Persian

53

PERSIAN™
Classy Cat Pokémon

PRONUNCIATION:	PURR-shin
TYPE:	Normal
HEIGHT:	1.0m WEIGHT: 32kg
ATTACKS:	Scratch, Growl, Bite, Pay Day, Screech
STRONG AGAINST:	None
WEAK AGAINST:	Rock, Steel
EVOLUTION:	Meowth=>Persian

54

PSYDUCK™
Duck Pokémon

PRONUNCIATION:	SYE-duck
TYPE:	Water
HEIGHT:	0.8m WEIGHT: 19.6kg
ATTACKS:	Scratch
STRONG AGAINST:	Fire, Ground, Rock
WEAK AGAINST:	Water, Grass, Dragon
EVOLUTION:	Psyduck=>Golduck

55

GOLDUCK™
Duck Pokémon

PRONUNCIATION:	GOAL-duck
TYPE:	Water
HEIGHT:	1.7m WEIGHT: 76.6kg
ATTACKS:	Scratch, Tail Whip, Disable
STRONG AGAINST:	Fire, Ground, Rock
WEAK AGAINST:	Water, Grass, Dragon
EVOLUTION:	Psyduck=>Golduck

56

MANKEY™
Pig Monkey Pokémon

PRONUNCIATION:	MANK-ee
TYPE:	Fighting
HEIGHT:	0.5m WEIGHT: 28kg
ATTACKS:	Scratch, Leer
STRONG AGAINST:	Normal, Ice, Rock, Dark, Steel
WEAK AGAINST:	Poison, Flying, Psychic, Bug
EVOLUTION:	Mankey=>Primeape

57

PRIMEAPE™
Pig Monkey Pokémon

PRONUNCIATION:	PRIME-ape
TYPE:	Fighting
HEIGHT:	1.0m WEIGHT: 32kg
ATTACKS:	Scratch, Leer, Karate Chop, Fury Swipes, Focus Energy
STRONG AGAINST:	Normal, Ice, Rock, Dark, Steel
WEAK AGAINST:	Poison, Flying, Psychic, Bug
EVOLUTION:	Mankey=>Primeape

58

GROWLITHE™
Puppy Pokémon

PRONUNCIATION:	GROWL-ith
TYPE:	Fire
HEIGHT:	0.7m WEIGHT: 19kg
ATTACKS:	Bite, Roar
STRONG AGAINST:	Grass, Ice, Bug,Steel
WEAK AGAINST:	Fire, Water, Rock, Dragon
EVOLUTION:	Growlithe=>Arcanine

59

ARCANINE™
Legendary Pokémon

PRONUNCIATION:	ar-Kuh-NINE
TYPE:	Fire
HEIGHT:	1.9m WEIGHT: 155kg
ATTACKS:	Roar, Leer, Take Down
STRONG AGAINST:	Grass, Ice, Bug,Steel
WEAK AGAINST:	Fire, Water, Rock, Dragon
EVOLUTION:	Growlithe=>Arcanine

60

POLIWAG™
Tadpole Pokémon

PRONUNCIATION:	POL-ee-wag
TYPE:	Water
HEIGHT:	0.6m WEIGHT: 12.4kg
ATTACKS:	Bubble
STRONG AGAINST:	Fire, Ground, Rock
WEAK AGAINST:	Water, Grass, Dragon
EVOLUTION:	Poliwag=>Poliwhirl

61

POLIWHIRL™
Tadpole Pokémon

PRONUNCIATION:	POL-ee-wurl
TYPE:	Water
HEIGHT:	1.0m WEIGHT: 20kg
ATTACKS:	Bubble, Hypnosis, Water Gun
STRONG AGAINST:	Fire, Ground, Rock
WEAK AGAINST:	Water, Grass, Dragon
EVOLUTION:	Poliwag=>Poliwhirl

POLIWRATH™
Tadpole Pokémon
PRONUNCIATION: POL-ee-rath
TYPE: Water/Fighting
HEIGHT: 1.3m **WEIGHT:** 54kg
ATTACKS: Doubleslap, Hypnosis, Water Gun
STRONG AGAINST: Fire, Ground, Rock, Normal, Ice, Dark, Steel
WEAK AGAINST: Water, Grass, Poison, Flying, Psychic, Bug
EVOLUTION: Poliwag=>Poliwhirl

ABRA™
PSI Pokémon
PRONUNCIATION: Ab-ruh
TYPE: Psychic
HEIGHT: 0.9m **WEIGHT:** 19.5kg
ATTACKS: Teleport
STRONG AGAINST: Fighting, Poison
WEAK AGAINST: Psychic, Steel
EVOLUTION: Abra=>Kadabra=> Alakazam

KADABRA™
PSI Pokémon
PRONUNCIATION: kah-DA-bruh
TYPE: Psychic
HEIGHT: 1.3m **WEIGHT:** 56.5kg
ATTACKS: Teleport, Confusion
STRONG AGAINST: Fighting, Poison
WEAK AGAINST: Psychic, Steel
EVOLUTION: Abra=>Kadabra=> Alakazam

ALAKAZAM™
PSI Pokémon
PRONUNCIATION: al-uh-kuh-ZAM
TYPE: Psychic
HEIGHT: 1.5m **WEIGHT:** 48kg
ATTACKS: Teleport, Confusion
STRONG AGAINST: Fighting, Poison
WEAK AGAINST: Psychic, Steel
EVOLUTION: Abra=>Kadabra=> Alakazam

MACHOP™
Superpower Pokémon
PRONUNCIATION: MAH-chop
TYPE: Fighting
HEIGHT: 0.8m **WEIGHT:** 19.5kg
ATTACKS: Karate Chop
STRONG AGAINST: Normal, Ice, Rock, Dark, Steel
WEAK AGAINST: Poison, Flying, Psychic, Bug
EVOLUTION: Machop=>Machoke=> Machamp

MACHOKE™
Superpower Pokémon
PRONUNCIATION: MAH-choke
TYPE: Fighting
HEIGHT: 1.5m **WEIGHT:** 70.5kg
ATTACKS: Karate Chop, Low Kick, Leer
STRONG AGAINST: Normal, Ice, Rock, Dark, Steel
WEAK AGAINST: Poison, Flying, Psychic, Bug
EVOLUTION: Machop=>Machoke=> Machamp

MACHAMP™
Superpower Pokémon
PRONUNCIATION: MAH-champ
TYPE: Fighting
HEIGHT: 1.6m **WEIGHT:** 130kg
ATTACKS: Karate Chop, Low Kick, Leer
STRONG AGAINST: Normal, Ice, Rock, Dark, Steel
WEAK AGAINST: Poison, Flying, Psychic, Bug
EVOLUTION: Machop=>Machoke=> Machamp

BELLSPROUT™
Flower Pokémon
PRONUNCIATION: BELL-sprout
TYPE: Grass/Poison
HEIGHT: 0.7m **WEIGHT:** 4kg
ATTACKS: Vine Whip, Growth
STRONG AGAINST: Grass, Water, Ground, Rock
WEAK AGAINST: Grass, Bug, Fire, Fighting, Flying, Poison, Ground, Rock, Ghost, Dark, Dragon, Steel
EVOLUTION: Bellsprout=>Weepinbell=> Victreebel

WEEPINBELL™
Flycatcher Pokémon
PRONUNCIATION: WEEP-in-bell
TYPE: Grass/Poison
HEIGHT: 1.0m **WEIGHT:** 6.4kg
ATTACKS: Vine Whip, Growth, Wrap, Poisonpowder, Sleep Powder
STRONG AGAINST: Grass, Water, Ground, Rock
WEAK AGAINST: Grass, Bug, Fire, Fighting, Flying, Poison, Ground, Rock, Ghost, Dark, Dragon, Steel
EVOLUTION: Bellsprout=>Weepinbell=> Victreebel

VICTREEBEL™
Flycatcher Pokémon
PRONUNCIATION: VICK-tree-bell
TYPE: Grass/Poison
HEIGHT: 1.7m **WEIGHT:** 15.5kg
ATTACKS: Sleep Powder, Razor Leaf
STRONG AGAINST: Grass, Water, Ground, Rock
WEAK AGAINST: Grass, Bug, Fire, Fighting, Flying, Poison, Ground, Rock, Ghost, Dark, Dragon, Steel
EVOLUTION: Bellsprout=>Weepinbell=> Victreebel

TENTACOOL™
Jellyfish Pokémon
PRONUNCIATION: TENT-uh-cool
TYPE: Water/Poison
HEIGHT: 0.9m **WEIGHT:** 45.5kg
ATTACKS: Acid
STRONG AGAINST: Fire, Ground, Rock, Grass
WEAK AGAINST: Water, Grass, Dragon, Poison, Ground, Rock, Ghost
EVOLUTION: Tentacool=>Tentacruel

TENTACRUEL™
Jellyfish Pokémon
PRONUNCIATION: TENT-uh-crool
TYPE: Water/Poison
HEIGHT: 1.6m **WEIGHT:** 55kg
ATTACKS: Supersonic, Poison Sting, Constrict
STRONG AGAINST: Fire, Ground, Rock, Grass
WEAK AGAINST: Water, Grass, Dragon, Poison, Ground, Rock, Ghost
EVOLUTION: Tentacool=>Tentacruel

GEODUDE™
Rock Pokémon
PRONUNCIATION: GEE-oh-dood
TYPE: Rock/Ground
HEIGHT: 0.4m **WEIGHT:** 20kg
ATTACKS: Tackle
STRONG AGAINST: Fire, Ice, Flying, Bug, Electric, Poison, Rock, Steel
WEAK AGAINST: Fighting, Ground, Steel, Grass, Bug
EVOLUTION: Geodude=>Graveler=> Golem

GRAVELER™
Rock Pokémon
PRONUNCIATION: GRAV-el-er
TYPE: Rock/Ground
HEIGHT: 1.0m **WEIGHT:** 105kg
ATTACKS: Tackle, Defence Curl, Rock Throw, Self Destruct
STRONG AGAINST: Fire, Ice, Flying, Bug, Electric, Poison, Rock, Steel
WEAK AGAINST: Fighting, Ground, Steel, Grass, Bug
EVOLUTION: Geodude=>Graveler=> Golem

GOLEM™
Megaton Pokémon
PRONUNCIATION: GOAL-um
TYPE: Rock/Ground
HEIGHT: 1.4m **WEIGHT:** 300kg
ATTACKS: Tackle, Defence Curl, Rock Throw, Self Destruct
STRONG AGAINST: Fire, Ice, Flying, Bug, Electric, Poison, Rock, Steel
WEAK AGAINST: Fighting, Ground, Steel, Grass, Bug
EVOLUTION: Geodude=>Graveler=> Golem

PONYTA™
Fire Horse Pokémon
PRONUNCIATION: po-NEE-tuh
TYPE: Fire
HEIGHT: 1.0m **WEIGHT:** 30kg
ATTACKS: Ember
STRONG AGAINST: Grass, Ice, Bug, Steel
WEAK AGAINST: Fire, Water, Rock, Dragon
EVOLUTION: Pontya=>Rapidash

RAPIDASH™
Fire Horse Pokémon
PRONUNCIATION: RAP-i-dash
TYPE: Fire
HEIGHT: 1.7m **WEIGHT:** 95kg
ATTACKS: Ember, Tail Whip, Stomp, Growl, Fire Spin
STRONG AGAINST: Grass, Ice, Bug, Steel
WEAK AGAINST: Fire, Water, Rock, Dragon
EVOLUTION: Pontya=>Rapidash

SLOWPOKE™
Dopey Pokémon
PRONUNCIATION: SLOW-poke
TYPE: Water/Psychic
HEIGHT: 1.2m **WEIGHT:** 36kg
ATTACKS: Confusion
STRONG AGAINST: Fire, Ground, Rock, Fighting, Poison
WEAK AGAINST: Water, Grass, Dragon, Pyschic, Steel
EVOLUTION: Slowpoke=>Slowbro Slowpoke=>Slowking

SLOWBRO™
Hermitcrab Pokémon

PRONUNCIATION:	SLOW-bro
TYPE:	Water/Psychic
HEIGHT:	1.6m WEIGHT: 78.5kg
ATTACKS:	Confusion, Disable,Growl, Water Gun, Withdraw
STRONG AGAINST:	Fire, Ground, Rock, Fighting, Poison
WEAK AGAINST:	Water, Grass, Dragon, Pyschic, Steel
EVOLUTION:	Slowpoke=>Slowbro

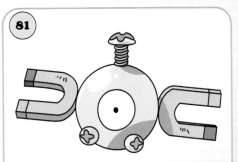

MAGNEMITE™
Magnet Pokémon

PRONUNCIATION:	MAG-nuh-mite
TYPE:	Electric/Steel
HEIGHT:	0.3m WEIGHT: 6kg
ATTACKS:	Tackle
STRONG AGAINST:	Water, Flying, Ice, Bug
WEAK AGAINST:	Electric, Grass, Dragon, Fire, Water
EVOLUTION:	Magnemite=>Magneton

MAGNETON™
Magnet Pokémon

PRONUNCIATION:	MAG-nuh-tun
TYPE:	Electric/Steel
HEIGHT:	1.0m WEIGHT: 60kg
ATTACKS:	Tackle, Sonicboom, Thundershock, Supersonic
STRONG AGAINST:	Water, Flying, Ice, Bug
WEAK AGAINST:	Electric, Grass, Dragon, Fire, Water
EVOLUTION:	Magnemite=>Magneton

FARFETCH'D™
Wild Duck Pokémon

PRONUNCIATION:	far-FETCHT
TYPE:	Normal/Flying
HEIGHT:	0.8m WEIGHT: 15kg
ATTACKS:	Peck, Sand Attack
STRONG AGAINST:	Grass, Fighting, Bug
WEAK AGAINST:	Rock, Steel, Electric
EVOLUTION:	None

DODUO™
Twin Bird Pokémon

PRONUNCIATION:	Doe-Doo-Oh
TYPE:	Normal/Flying
HEIGHT:	1.4m WEIGHT: 39.2kg
ATTACKS:	Peck
STRONG AGAINST:	Grass, Fighting, Bug
WEAK AGAINST:	Rock, Steel, Electric
EVOLUTION:	Doduo=>Dodrio

DODRIO™
Triplebird Pokémon

PRONUNCIATION:	doe-DREE-oh
TYPE:	Normal/Flying
HEIGHT:	1.8m WEIGHT: 85.2kg
ATTACKS:	Peck, Growl, Fury Attack, Drill Peck
STRONG AGAINST:	Grass, Fighting, Bug
WEAK AGAINST:	Rock, Steel, Electric
EVOLUTION:	Doduo=>Dodrio

SEEL™
Sea Lion Pokémon

PRONUNCIATION:	seel
TYPE:	Water
HEIGHT:	1.1m WEIGHT: 90kg
ATTACKS:	Headbutt
STRONG AGAINST:	Fire, Ground, Rock
WEAK AGAINST:	Water, Grass, Dragon
EVOLUTION:	Seel=>Dewgong

DEWGONG™
Sea Lion Pokémon

PRONUNCIATION:	DOO-gong
TYPE:	Water/Ice
HEIGHT:	1.7m WEIGHT: 120kg
ATTACKS:	Headbutt, Growl
STRONG AGAINST:	Fire, Ground, Rock, Grass, Flying, Dragon
WEAK AGAINST:	Water, Grass, Dragon, Fire, Ice, Steel
EVOLUTION:	Seel=>Dewgong

GRIMER™
Sludge Pokémon

PRONUNCIATION:	GRIME-er
TYPE:	Poison
HEIGHT:	0.9m WEIGHT: 30kg
ATTACKS:	Pound, Disable
STRONG AGAINST:	Grass
WEAK AGAINST:	Poison, Ground, Rock, Ghost
EVOLUTION:	Grimer=>Muk

89

MUK™
Sludge Pokémon
PRONUNCIATION: GRIME-er
TYPE: Poison
HEIGHT: 1.2m WEIGHT: 30kg
ATTACKS: Pound, Disable, Poison Gas, Sludge
STRONG AGAINST: Grass
WEAK AGAINST: Poison, Ground, Rock, Ghost
EVOLUTION: Grimer=>Muk

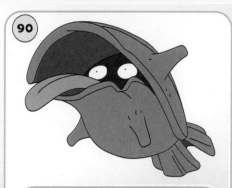

90

SHELLDER™
Bivalve Pokémon
PRONUNCIATION: SHELL-der
TYPE: Water
HEIGHT: 0.3m WEIGHT: 4kg
ATTACKS: Tackle, Withdraw
STRONG AGAINST: Fire, Ground, Rock
WEAK AGAINST: Water, Grass, Dragon
EVOLUTION: Shellder=>Cloyster

91

CLOYSTER™
Bivalve Pokémon
PRONUNCIATION: CLOY-stir
TYPE: Water/Ice
HEIGHT: 1.5m WEIGHT: 1332.5kg
ATTACKS: Withdraw, Supersonic, Aurora Beam
STRONG AGAINST: Fire, Ground, Rock, Grass, Flying, Dragon
WEAK AGAINST: Water, Grass, Dragon, Fire, Ice, Steel
EVOLUTION: Shellder=>Cloyster

92

GASTLY™
Gas Pokémon
PRONUNCIATION: GAST-lee
TYPE: Ghost/Poison
HEIGHT: 1.3m WEIGHT: 0.1kg
ATTACKS: Lick, Confuse Ray, Night Shade
STRONG AGAINST: Pyschic, Ghost, Grass
WEAK AGAINST: Dark, Steel, Poison, Ground, Rock, Ghost
EVOLUTION: Gastly=>Haunter=>Gengar

93

HAUNTER™
Gas Pokémon
PRONUNCIATION: HAWN-ter
TYPE: Ghost/Poison
HEIGHT: 1.6m WEIGHT: 0.1kg
ATTACKS: Lick, Confuse Ray, Night Shade
STRONG AGAINST: Pyschic, Ghost, Grass
WEAK AGAINST: Dark, Steel, Poison, Ground, Rock, Ghost
EVOLUTION: Gastly=>Haunter=>Gengar

94

GENGAR™
Shadow Pokémon
PRONUNCIATION: GANG-are
TYPE: Ghost/Poison
HEIGHT: 1.5m WEIGHT: 40.5kg
ATTACKS: Lick, Confuse Ray, Night Shade
STRONG AGAINST: Pyschic, Ghost, Grass
WEAK AGAINST: Dark, Steel, Poison, Ground, Rock, Ghost
EVOLUTION: Gastly=>Haunter=>Gengar

95

ONIX™
Rock Snake Pokémon
PRONUNCIATION: Ohnicks
TYPE: Rock/Ground
HEIGHT: 8.8m WEIGHT: 210kg
ATTACKS: Tackle, Screech
STRONG AGAINST: Fire, Ice, Flying, Bug, Electric, Poison, Rock, Steel
WEAK AGAINST: Fighting, Ground, Steel, Grass, Bug
EVOLUTION: Onix=>Steelix

96

DROWZEE™
Hypnosis Pokémon
PRONUNCIATION: Drow-zee
TYPE: Psychic
HEIGHT: 1.0m WEIGHT: 32.4kg
ATTACKS: Pound, Hypnosis
STRONG AGAINST: Fighting, Poison
WEAK AGAINST: Psychic, Steel
EVOLUTION: Drowzee=>Hypno

97

HYPNO™
Hypnosis Pokémon
PRONUNCIATION: HIP-no
TYPE: Psychic
HEIGHT: 1.6m WEIGHT: 75.6kg
ATTACKS: Pound, Hypnosis, Disable, Confusion, Headbutt
STRONG AGAINST: Fighting, Poison
WEAK AGAINST: Psychic, Steel
EVOLUTION: Drowzee=>Hypno

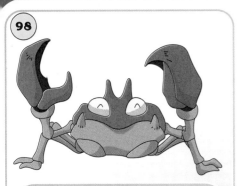

98
KRABBY™
River Crab Pokémon

PRONUNCIATION:	CRA-bee
TYPE:	Water
HEIGHT:	1.6m WEIGHT: 32.4kg
ATTACKS:	Bubble, Leer
STRONG AGAINST:	Fire, Ground, Rock
WEAK AGAINST:	Water, Grass, Dragon
EVOLUTION:	Kabby=>Kingler

99
KINGLER™
Pincer Crab Pokémon

PRONUNCIATION:	KING-ler
TYPE:	Water
HEIGHT:	1.3m WEIGHT: 60kg
ATTACKS:	Bubble, Leer, Vicegrip,Guillotine
STRONG AGAINST:	Fire, Ground, Rock
WEAK AGAINST:	Water, Grass, Dragon
EVOLUTION:	Kabby=>Kingler

100
VOLTORB™
Ball Pokémon

PRONUNCIATION:	VOL-torb
TYPE:	Electric
HEIGHT:	0.5m WEIGHT: 10.4kg
ATTACKS:	Tackle, Screech
STRONG AGAINST:	Water, Flying
WEAK AGAINST:	Electric, Grass, Dragon
EVOLUTION:	Voltorb=>Electrode

101
ELECTRODE™
Ball Pokémon

PRONUNCIATION:	ee-LECK-trode
TYPE:	Electric
HEIGHT:	0.5m WEIGHT: 66.6kg
ATTACKS:	Tackle, Screech
STRONG AGAINST:	Water, Flying
WEAK AGAINST:	Electric, Grass, Dragon
EVOLUTION:	Voltorb=>Electrode

102
EXEGGCUTE™
Egg Pokémon

PRONUNCIATION:	EGGS-egg-cute
TYPE:	Grass/Psychic
HEIGHT:	0.4m WEIGHT: 2.5kg
ATTACKS:	Barrage, Hypnosis
STRONG AGAINST:	Water, Ground, Rock, Fighting, Poison
WEAK AGAINST:	Fire, Grass, Poison, Flying, Bug, Dragon, Psychic, Steel
EVOLUTION:	Exeggcute=>Exeggutor

103
EXEGGUTOR™
Coconut Pokémon

PRONUNCIATION:	eggs-EGG-you-tor
TYPE:	Grass/Psychic
HEIGHT:	2.0m WEIGHT: 120kg lbs
ATTACKS:	Barrage, Hypnosis
STRONG AGAINST:	Water, Ground, Rock, Fighting, Poison
WEAK AGAINST:	Fire, Grass, Poison, Flying, Bug, Dragon, Psychic, Steel
EVOLUTION:	Exeggcute=>Exeggutor

104
CUBONE™
Lonely Pokémon

PRONUNCIATION:	CUE-bone
TYPE:	Ground
HEIGHT:	0.4m WEIGHT: 6.5kg
ATTACKS:	Bone Club, Growl
STRONG AGAINST:	Electric, Fire, Poison, Rock, Steel
WEAK AGAINST:	Grass, Bug
EVOLUTION:	Cubone=>Marowak

105
MAROWAK™
Bonekeeper Pokémon

PRONUNCIATION:	MAR-row-ack
TYPE:	Ground
HEIGHT:	1.0m WEIGHT: 45kg
ATTACKS:	Focus Energy, Thrash, Bonemerang, Rage
STRONG AGAINST:	Electric, Fire, Poison, Rock, Steel
WEAK AGAINST:	Grass, Bug
EVOLUTION:	Cubone=>Marowak

106
HITMONLEE™
Kicking Pokémon

PRONUNCIATION:	HI-mon-lee
TYPE:	Fighting
HEIGHT:	1.5m WEIGHT: 49.8kg
ATTACKS:	Double Kick, Meditate
STRONG AGAINST:	Normal, Ice, Rock, Dark, Steel
WEAK AGAINST:	Poison, Flying, Psychic, Bug
EVOLUTION:	Hitmonlee=>Hitmonchan

CONTINUED ON PAGE 78

Pokémon

ASH-TONISHING!

OH, NO! Those rotten Team Rocket have used a weapon on my Poké Balls, and six of my current Pokémon have escaped and evolved to the their different levels, all at the same time! Can you match the Pokémon to their different evolutions so I can recapture them? Remember, some Pokémon can evolve three times, others only twice!

48

PICHU

SKIPLOOM

AMPHAROS

HOPPIP

FLAAFFY

FERALIGATR

MAREEP

CROCONAW

RAICHU

TOTODILE

PIKACHU

JUMPLUFF

POKÉMON
POKÉMON CREATOR

Hey, Pokémon dudes! If you were pulled into Pokémon world, what sort of Pokémon would you like as a companion? Using your imagination, draw your ideal Pokémon and then colour your picture!

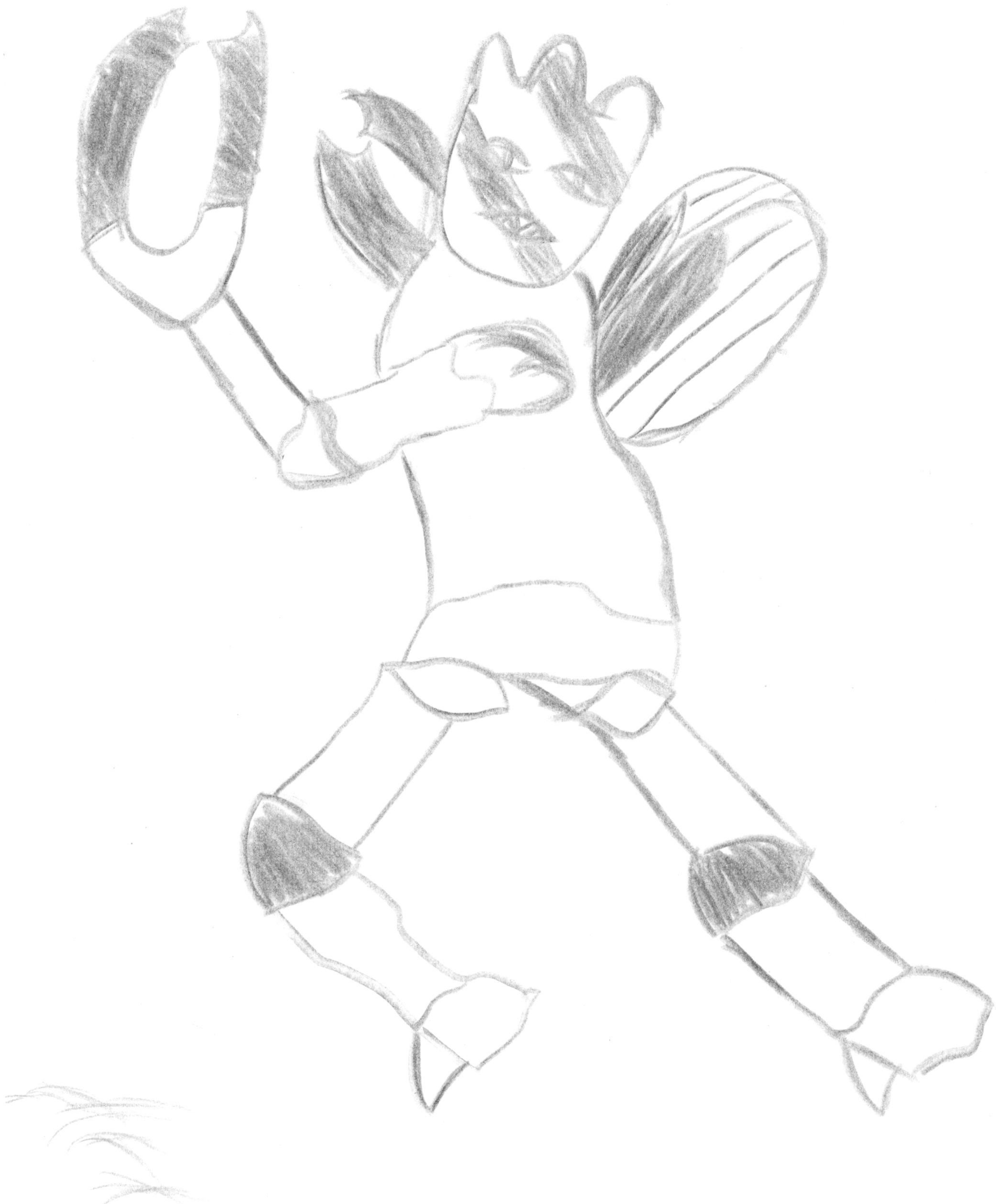

ELECTRIC SHOCK SHOWDOWN

One day, after being lost for two whole weeks, Ash, Misty and Brock finally reached beautiful Vermilion City.

"I can't wait to take a bubble bath!" exclaimed Misty.
"I have to hit the laundromat!" said Brock. But Ash had other plans and announced, "I'm going to find the Vermilion City Gym right now!"
Just then, Pikachu sat down on the ground. It

was so hungry that it couldn't walk another step! That's when everyone realised how hungry they were, too – so, with Pikachu in Ash's arms, they headed straight to the Pokémon Centre for a big meal.

Just as the friends arrived at the Pokémon Centre, a wounded Rattata was rushed in on a stretcher. "That's the fifteenth Pokémon brought in this month," remarked Joy, the Pokémon Centre's nurse. "They all lost to Lieutenant Surge, the Vermilion Gym leader."

Pikachu didn't like the sound of that! "Pika! Pika!" it cried. "Don't be scared, Pikachu," said Ash. "You won't end up that way, because you'll win!" But Pikachu wasn't so sure.

After everyone had eaten and rested, they made their way to the Vermilion City Gym.

"Hello?" called Ash, as he opened the door. "I've come for a Pokémon battle, to earn a Thunder Badge."

A man came to the door and looked a Ash.

"Hey, Boss," he sneered. "Here's another victim for the emergency room!" Lieutenant Surge appeared. "Humph! Which one?" he asked.

Ash, Misty and Brock gasped. Lieutenant Surge was huge! How could Ash possibly win against him?

Lieutenant Surge laughed when he saw Pikachu trying to hide behind Ash's leg. "What? A Pikachu? Look at this – Baby brought along a baby Pokémon."

"Quit it!" said Ash. "My name's Ash Ketchum, not Baby. Why are you making fun of my Pikachu?"

"I'll show you why," said Surge. "Go, Poké Ball!" Surge hurled the Poké Ball and out came a large creature.

"It's a Raichu!" said Ash, taking out his Pokédex.

"Raichu," said the mechanical voice of Dexter. "A mouse Pokémon of the Electric Type. Raichu is the evolved form of Pikachu and it can shock with more than 100,000 volts."

Pikachu growled at Raichu.

"There's no way we're going to quit now!" announced Ash, hiding how nervous he was. Pikachu was nervous too – but it was just as determined as Ash.

"What could a baby like that Pikachu do?" Sneered Surge. "If you want to become a Pokémon Master, you should make your Pokémon evolve as soon as you catch it."

"There's more to raising a Pokémon than forcing it to evolve! And I like this Pikachu just the way it is!" said Ash.
"Wrong, Baby – electric Pokémon are only useful once they've learned all their different electrical attacks. If you keep it puny like that, it's no more than a pet," remarked Surge.
That comment made Pikachu mad – and ready for action! But even Brock and Misty doubted that Pikachu could win a battle against Raichu.
"Let the battle begin!" called he announcer.

"Raichu! Show 'em real thundershock!" ordered Surge.
"Rai ... CHU!" cried Raichu, sending out a powerful shock.
Pikachu hit the ground with a thud.
"Call Pikachu back, Ash!" said Brock.
"This is a mismatch."
"Pikachu, return!" ordered Ash. But Pikachu refused. It didn't want to stop until it had beaten Raichu! Brave little Pikachu did its best, but

it was no match for Raichu. Raichu easily overpowered Pikachu with thunder punches and thunder kicks. Watching through a window was Team Rocket. As they watched Pikachu struggle, they began to wonder if Pikachu was worth stealing, after all!

The match was over in no time. Ash picked up Pikachu and took it to the Pokémon Centre for some rest.

"Pikachu's spirit got hurt pretty badly," observed Brock. "It was totally overpowered by that Raichu."

But Ash said, "We'll win next time if Pikachu tries harder."

Misty shook her head and said softly, "I think Pikachu was trying its best the last time."

That's when Nurse Joy
appeared.
"A while ago, I just happened
to come across this," said Joy,
holding out a special stone.
"It's a Thunder Stone," said
Brock. "You can use it to make
Pikachu evolve into a Raichu."
"Then Pikachu might be strong
enough to win," said Ash.
"You've got to think hard
before using the Thunder
Stone," advised Joy.

"Remember, Ash, if you make Pikachu evolve, you can't change it back,"
warned Misty.
"Pikachu will never be the same," added Brock.
Ash turned to Pikachu and said quietly, "Pikachu, if you
become a Raichu, I might be able to win. But to make you
evolve just to fight ... I would be as bad as Surge.
Pikachu, what do you want to do? I don't want to
force you to evolve if you'd rather stay
the way you are now."
Everyone looked at Pikachu as it lay in bed.
What would Pikachu decide?

Meanwhile, Team Rocket spied on the group from the waiting room.
"Ash is letting Pikachu decide," whispered Jessie. They watched as Pikachu stood up – and kicked the Thunder Stone out of Ash's hand!
Meowth translated Pikachu's words. "It's so brave!" said Meowth.

"Pikachu won't change. Pikachu says if it's going to get Raichu it wants to do it just as it is ... it's going to fight in the name of all Pikachu!"

Ash and Pikachu vowed to beat Raichu together. They realised, with Brock's help, that Raichu did have weaknesses – from evolving too soon. So they planned a good strategy with that in mind.

After Pikachu had a long rest, Ash and his friends took it back to the gym for the rematch with Surge and Raichu. Team Rocket was there, too – spying from outside again.
"Use the strategy we planned, Pikachu! You can do it!" coached Ash.

"Go, Raichu!" called Surge. Raichu shocked Pikachu and lashed it with its electric tail! Then Raichu delivered a body slam on Pikachu. But when Raichu tried another body slam, Pikachu was ready.

"Chu!" cried Pikachu, rolling quickly out of the way. Raichu crashed to the ground!

"The strategy is working!" cried Misty. "Right" replied Brock. "Raichu evolved too fast and it never learned the speed attacks that it could learn only in the Pikachu stage!"

"Pikachu! Agility now!" ordered Ash. Pikachu delivered its agility attacks on Raichu, who soon tired of dodging Pikachu's quick, darting moves.

"Your Raichu's way too slow, Surge! That's its weakness!" called Ash. Surge ignored Ash and shouted, "Ok, Raichu! Give it a thunderbolt! Shut it down!"

"Rai ... CHU!" cried Raichu, sending out a powerful thundershock. CRASH! The thundershock shattered the windows of the gym!

61

"Way to go!" shouted Brock. "Pikachu used its tail as a ground, and dodged the electric shock!"

"Rai? Rai? Rai?" cried Raichu, sending out sputtering shocks. Raichu was out of electricity!

"All right!" shouted Ash. "Pikachu, quick attack now!"

Pikachu delivered a quick attack ... and another! Now Raichu was so weak that it could barely move. The match was over!

"We did it, Pikachu!" shouted Ash.
"Congratulations! Well done, Ash and Pikachu! As proof of your victory ... a Thunder Badge! You should be proud – you and your Pikachu fought well together," said Surge admiringly. He handed the badge to Ash.

"Thanks," said Ash. "Wow! A Thunder Badge – and it's all mine!" Even Raichu clapped in admiration.

Ash swept Pikachu into his arms and held it close.
"Thank you, Pikachu!" he said. "This was your victory!"
"Pika! Pika!" cried Pikachu happily.
Meanwhile, Team Rocket decided that Pikachu was worth stealing after all, and so the adventures continued ...

POKÉMON
THE GREAT ESCAPE!

OH, NO! Team Rocket have stolen all of Ash's Poké Balls and kidnapped Pikachu! But you know Ash won't take this lying down and Team Rocket are in for a bruising! Ash is on their trail even as I speak! He's found a map of a maze Team Rocket are hiding in, and knows he can pick up spare Poké Balls along the way! Of the four entrances that lead to the middle of the maze, can you find the one that allows Ash to collect the most Poké Balls so that he can give Team Rocket a good hiding?

64

POKéMON SPLIT UP!

Copy Picture into Grid

I've heard of people 'going to pieces' but this is ridiculous! Can you copy the drawings on the numbered squares into the corresponding numbers of the grid to put Ash and Pikachu back together again? Afterwards, put some colour back into their cheeks by colouring in the picture!

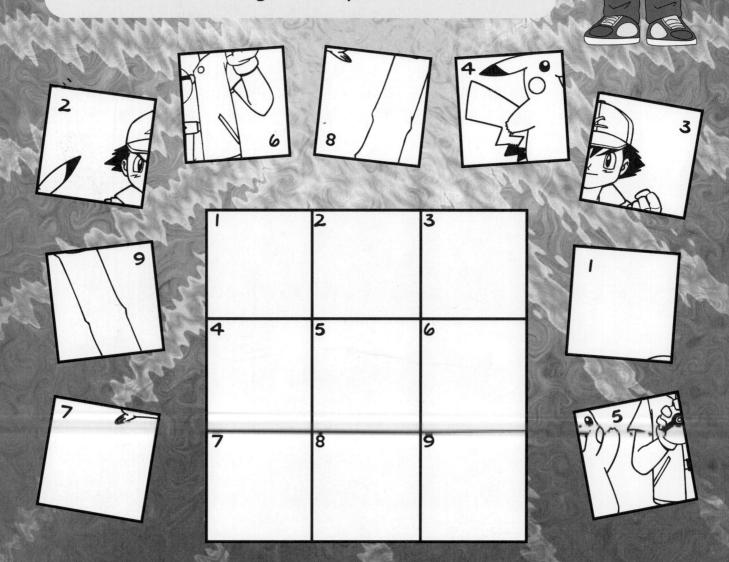

POKéMON

DAY OF THE DONPHAN!

Ash, Pikachu, Misty and Brock were on their way to Violet City. Ash, on his way to take part in the Johto League, was looking for new Pokémon trainers to battle in his quest to become the greatest Pokémon Master of all!

Climbing to the top of a rocky hill, they saw a strange-looking creature on the other side, all alone. "Guys!" squealed Misty in delight. "It's a Pokémon!" Ash quickly switched on his Pokédex and heard Dexter's voice boom out.

"Donphan," the Dexter informed them. "The Armour Pokémon. With it's strong tusks and tough skin, Donphan is known for it's powerful Tackle Attack. The length of Donphan's tusks indicates its level."

"Sounds good to me!" cried Ash, excitedly. "Now all I gotta do is catch it!"

Before Ash could move, Brock was already rushing down towards the Donphan! He had decided that, because this Donphan had small tusks, he, as a breeder, should look after it!

"Onix," he shouted, throwing his Poké Ball. "GOOOOO!" As the Poké B.all opened, an Onix burst free, and tried to knock Donphan over with a Tackle Attack!

But to Brock's amazement, Donphan moved so fast, Onix completely missed him and crashed into a tree! WHAAAAM! This was Ash's chance!
"I choose you... Heracross!" he yelled, throwing a Poké Ball.

Heracross, Ash's new Pokémon appeared, and with it's incredibly strong Horn Attack, lifted up the surprised Donphan and threw it off it's feet!

Suddenly, a young girl named Rochelle, appeared. "That's enough!" she cried, rushing over to Donphan to protect it. "This Donphan belongs to me!"

Rochelle explained that she trained Donphan from young to sniff out a gemstone known as Ambernite, a gemstone so rare it was more valuable than gold or diamonds! One such as she was wearing in her broach.

Apologising For their mistakes, the friends said goodbye to Rochelle and continued on their journey. Unfortunately for Rochelle, Team Rocket were in the area!

They were searching for Ambernite to make themselves zillionaires! Overhearing Rochelle explain that Donphan could sniff out the gemstone, they wanted one!

"Fury swipes!" hissed Meowth, attacking Rochelle's Donphan, and knocking it senseless! "Nooo!" cried a helpless Rochelle, as Jessie

grabbed the stunned
Donphan and Team Rocket
ran off!

Desperate to find
her lost Donphan,
Rochelle scoured the
area, eventually
meeting up again
with Ash and his
friends. After she
had explained what
had happened, Ash released
his Zubat, in the hopes of
locating the missing Donphan.
"It's no use, guys," he said
after awhile. "Zubat's
Supersonic isn't
working out here...there
are too many trees and the

sound gets deflected!" Rochelle
drew out a whistle and blew,
very loudly. Suddenly, a whole
herd of adult Donphan
appeared!
"I train all these Donphan with
this whistle," she explained.
"Unfortunately, I haven't had time
to train my youngest Donphan yet!
But these Donphan will be able to find
their missing friend!"

And find her they did! Team Rocket had just discovered, to their dismay, that the Donphan they had kidnapped had not yet been trained yet to find Ambernite, when they found themselves surrounded by a herd of angry Donphan!

"Give that Donphan back!" demanded Ash, but Team Rocket was in the mood for a fight! They released Arbok and Victreebel, just as Brock attacked with Onix! Victreebel's Wrap Attack and Sleep Powder Attack brought Onix crashing down to the ground, unconscious! "Okay," growled Ash. "Now it's our turn!"

"Waaaah!" squealed James, as Ash commanded Pikachu to release his Thunderbolt Attack and Team Rocket was zapped by Pikachu's electrifying lightning powers! KKKRRAKKKKLE!! They flew threw the air to crash painfully down on the ground! THUMMMP!

Defeated, Team Rocket made good their escape! To thank Ash for his help, Rochelle agreed to battle him with one of her adult Donphan! "I choose you, Heracross!" cried Ash, as Heracross charged in with his Tackle Attack!

Heracross then used his Endure to throw the Donphan, but it quickly recovered! "Donphan, show 'em your Roll Out Attack!" cried Rochelle, and the Donphan rolled itself over, knocking Heracross flat!

"You didn't win this time, Ash," said Rochelle, after the battle. "It takes time for a Pokémon to get to know its trainer and become the best that it can be! But you and Heracross make a great team! And Heracross certainly is strong!"

Ash beamed happily. "That's true," he chuckled. "We just need a little more training! Don't worry, Heracross...pretty soon, you'll be unbeatable!"

A grateful Rochelle bid a fond farewell to her new friends as they headed once again for Violet City. And though Ash and Heracross may have lost the battle, they both gained valuable experience. That experience would help prepare them for the challenges that lay ahead in their journey to the Johto League!

POKÉMON
GOING DOTTY!

Oh, dear! Squirtle's exhausted from all the training and battles Ash has been putting it through - it's not only seeing spots before the eyes, it's turned all spotty himself!

Can you join up the dots and put Squirtle back together again?
Afterwards, colour in the picture.

POKéMON
Name That Pokémon

A good Pokémon Master knows their Pokémon like the back of their hand. Play this memory game with a friend. Study the Pokémon on these pages for 30 seconds, then close the book and write down all the Pokémon you can remember. You will get a point for each one you get right! There are a few new ones so no cheating now!

BLASTOISE

SMOOCHUM

SKARMORY

ODDISH

SQUIRTLE

CLEFABLE

ELECTABUZZ

CHARMANDER

MACHAMP

BUTTERFREE

POINTS

1-3:   Are you sure you're not a Pokémon traitor in disguise?

4-6:   Go and join Team Rocket. They need another someone like you to join their gang!

7-9:   Keep up that Pokémon training - you've got a long way to go yet!

10:    Wow! You really are a Pokémon Master! Well done!

107

HITMONCHAN™
Punching Pokémon

PRONUNCIATION:	HIT-mon-chan
TYPE:	Fighting
HEIGHT:	1.4m WEIGHT: 50.2kg
ATTACKS:	Comet Punch, Agility
STRONG AGAINST:	Normal, Ice, Rock, Dark, Steel
WEAK AGAINST:	Poison, Flying, Psychic, Bug
EVOLUTION:	Hitmonlee=>Hitmonchan

108

LICKITUNG™
Licking Pokémon

PRONUNCIATION:	LICK-i-tung
TYPE:	Normal
HEIGHT:	1.2m WEIGHT: 65.5kg
ATTACKS:	Wrap, Supersonic
STRONG AGAINST:	None
WEAK AGAINST:	Rock, Steel
EVOLUTION:	None

109

KOFFING™
Poison Gas Pokémon

PRONUNCIATION:	CAWF-ing
TYPE:	Poison
HEIGHT:	0.6m WEIGHT: 1kg
ATTACKS:	Tackle, Smog
STRONG AGAINST:	Grass
WEAK AGAINST:	Poison, Ground, Rock, Ghost
EVOLUTION:	Koffing=>Weezing

110

WEEZING™
Poison Gas Pokémon

PRONUNCIATION:	WEEZE-ing
TYPE:	Poison
HEIGHT:	1.2m WEIGHT: 9.5kg
ATTACKS:	Tackle, Smog, Sludge
STRONG AGAINST:	Grass
WEAK AGAINST:	Poison, Ground, Rock, Ghost
EVOLUTION:	Koffing=>Weezing

111

RHYHORN™
Spikes Pokémon

PRONUNCIATION:	RYE-horn
TYPE:	Ground/Rock
HEIGHT:	1.0m WEIGHT: 115kg
ATTACKS:	Horn Attack
STRONG AGAINST:	Fire, Electric, Poison, Rock, Steel, Ice, Flying, Bug
WEAK AGAINST:	Grass, Bug, Fighting, Ground, Steel
EVOLUTION:	Rhyhorn=>Rhydon

112

RHYDON™
Drill Pokémon

PRONUNCIATION:	RYE-donn
TYPE:	Ground/Rock
HEIGHT:	1.9m WEIGHT: 120kg
ATTACKS:	Horn Attack, Stomp, Tail Whip, Fury Attack
STRONG AGAINST:	Fire, Electric, Poison, Rock, Steel, Ice, Flying, Bug
WEAK AGAINST:	Grass, Bug, Fighting, Ground, Steel
EVOLUTION:	Rhyhorn=>Rhydon

113

CHANSEY™
Egg Pokémon

PRONUNCIATION:	CHAN-see
TYPE:	Normal
HEIGHT:	1.1m WEIGHT: 34.6kg
ATTACKS:	Pound, Doubleslap
STRONG AGAINST:	None
WEAK AGAINST:	Rock, Steel
EVOLUTION:	Chansey=>Blissey

114

TANGELA™
Vine Pokémon

PRONUNCIATION:	TANG-guh-luh
TYPE:	Grass
HEIGHT:	1.0m WEIGHT: 35kg
ATTACKS:	Constrict, Bind
STRONG AGAINST:	Water, Ground, Rock
WEAK AGAINST:	Fire, Grass, Poison, Flying, Bug, Dragon, Steel
EVOLUTION:	None

115

KANGASKHAN™
Parent Pokémon

PRONUNCIATION:	KANG-guh-con
TYPE:	Normal
HEIGHT:	2.2m WEIGHT: 80kg
ATTACKS:	Comet Punch, Rage
STRONG AGAINST:	None
WEAK AGAINST:	Rock, Steel
EVOLUTION:	None

116

HORSEA™
Dragon Pokémon

PRONUNCIATION:	HORSE-ee
TYPE:	Water
HEIGHT:	0.4m WEIGHT: 8kg
ATTACKS:	Bubble
STRONG AGAINST:	Fire, Ground, Rock
WEAK AGAINST:	Water, Grass, Dragon
EVOLUTION:	Horsea=>Seadra=> Kingdra

117

SEADRA™
Dragon Pokémon

PRONUNCIATION:	SEE-druh
TYPE:	Water
HEIGHT:	1.2m WEIGHT: 25kg
ATTACKS:	Bubble, Leer, Smokescreen, Water Gun
STRONG AGAINST:	Fire, Ground, Rock
WEAK AGAINST:	Water, Grass, Dragon
EVOLUTION:	Horsea=>Seadra=> Kingdra

118

GOLDEEN™
Goldfish Pokémon

PRONUNCIATION:	GOAL-deen
TYPE:	Water
HEIGHT:	0.6m WEIGHT: 15kg
ATTACKS:	Peck, Tail Whip
STRONG AGAINST:	Fire, Ground, Rock
WEAK AGAINST:	Water, Grass, Dragon
EVOLUTION:	Goldeen=>Seaking

119

SEAKING™
Goldfish Pokémon

PRONUNCIATION:	SEE-king
TYPE:	Water
HEIGHT:	1.3m WEIGHT: 39kg
ATTACKS:	Peck, Tail Whip, Supersonic
STRONG AGAINST:	Fire, Ground, Rock
WEAK AGAINST:	Water, Grass, Dragon
EVOLUTION:	Goldeen=>Seaking

120

STARYU™
Starshape Pokémon

PRONUNCIATION:	STAR-you
TYPE:	Water
HEIGHT:	0.8m WEIGHT: 34.5kg
ATTACKS:	Tackle
STRONG AGAINST:	Fire, Ground, Rock
WEAK AGAINST:	Water, Grass, Dragon
EVOLUTION:	Staryu=>Starmie

121

STARMIE™
Mysterious Pokémon

PRONUNCIATION:	star-ME
TYPE:	Water/Psychic
HEIGHT:	1.1m WEIGHT: 80kg
ATTACKS:	Tackle
STRONG AGAINST:	Fire, Ground, Rock, Fighting, Poison
WEAK AGAINST:	Water, Grass, Dragon, Psychic, Steel
EVOLUTION:	Staryu=>Starmie

122

MR. MIME™
Barrier Pokémon

PRONUNCIATION:	MIS-ter MIME
TYPE:	Psychic
HEIGHT:	1.3m WEIGHT: 54.5kg
ATTACKS:	Confusion, Barrier
STRONG AGAINST:	Fighting, Poison
WEAK AGAINST:	Psychic, Steel
EVOLUTION:	None

123

SCYTHER™
Mantis Pokémon

PRONUNCIATION:	SYE-ther
TYPE:	Bug/Flying
HEIGHT:	1.5m WEIGHT: 56kg
ATTACKS:	Quick Attack
STRONG AGAINST:	Grass, Psychic, Dark, Fighting, Bug
WEAK AGAINST:	Fire, Fighting, Flying, Ghost, Steel, Electric, Rock
EVOLUTION:	Scyther=>Scizor

124

JYNX™
Humanshape Pokémon

PRONUNCIATION:	JINCKS
TYPE:	Ice/Psychic
HEIGHT:	1.4m WEIGHT: 40.6kg
ATTACKS:	Pound, Lovely Kiss
STRONG AGAINST:	Grass, Ground, Flying, Dragon, Fighting, Poison
WEAK AGAINST:	Fire, Water, Ice, Steel, Pyschic
EVOLUTION:	Smoochum=>Jynx

125 ELECTABUZZ™
Electric Pokémon

PRONUNCIATION: uh-LECK-tuh-buzz
TYPE: Electric
HEIGHT: 1.1m   WEIGHT: 30kg
ATTACKS: Quick Attack, Leer
STRONG AGAINST: Water, Flying
WEAK AGAINST: Electric, Grass, Dragon
EVOLUTION: Elekid=>Electabuzz

126 MAGMAR™
Spitfire Pokémon

PRONUNCIATION: MAG-mar
TYPE: Fire
HEIGHT: 1.3m   WEIGHT: 44.5kg
ATTACKS: Ember
STRONG AGAINST: Grass, Ice, Bug, Steel
WEAK AGAINST: Fire, Water, Rock, Dragon
EVOLUTION: Magby=>Magmar

127 PINSIR™
Stagbeetle Pokémon

PRONUNCIATION: PIN-sir
TYPE: Bug
HEIGHT: 1.5m   WEIGHT: 55kg
ATTACKS: Vicegrip
STRONG AGAINST: Grass, Psychic, Dark
WEAK AGAINST: Ghost, Flying, Fighting, Fire, Dark
EVOLUTION: None

128 TAUROS™
Wild Bull Pokémon

PRONUNCIATION: TOR-ose
TYPE: Normal
HEIGHT: 1.4m   WEIGHT: 88.4kg
ATTACKS: Tackle
STRONG AGAINST: None
WEAK AGAINST: Rock, Steel
EVOLUTION: None

129 MAGIKARP™
Fish Pokémon

PRONUNCIATION: mag-i-KARP
TYPE: Water
HEIGHT: 0.9m   WEIGHT: 10kg
ATTACKS: Splash
STRONG AGAINST: Fire, Ground, Rock
WEAK AGAINST: Water, Grass, Dragon
EVOLUTION: Magikarp=>Gyarados

130 GYARADOS™
Atrocious Pokémon

PRONUNCIATION: GAR-i-dose
TYPE: Water/Flying
HEIGHT: 6.5m   WEIGHT: 235kg
ATTACKS: Thrash, Bite, Dragon Rage
STRONG AGAINST: Fire, Ground, Rock, Grass, Fighting, Bug
WEAK AGAINST: Water, Grass, Dragon, Electric, Rock
EVOLUTION: Magikarp=>Gyarados

131 LAPRAS™
Transport Pokémon

PRONUNCIATION: LAP-russ
TYPE: Water/Ice
HEIGHT: 2.5m   WEIGHT: 220kg
ATTACKS: Water Gun, Growl
STRONG AGAINST: Fire, Ground, Rock, Grass, Ground, Flying, Dragon
WEAK AGAINST: Water, Grass, Dragon, Fire, Ice, Steel
EVOLUTION: None

132 DITTO™
Transform Pokémon

PRONUNCIATION: DID-oh
TYPE: Normal
HEIGHT: 0.3m   WEIGHT: 4kg
ATTACKS: Transform
STRONG AGAINST: None
WEAK AGAINST: Rock, Steel
EVOLUTION: None

133 EEVEE™
Evolution Pokémon

PRONUNCIATION: EE-vee
TYPE: Normal
HEIGHT: 0.3m   WEIGHT: 6.5kg
ATTACKS: Tackle, Sand-Attack
STRONG AGAINST: None
WEAK AGAINST: Rock, Steel
EVOLUTION: Eevee =>Vaporeon
Eevee=>Jolteon Eevee=>Flareon
Eevee=>Espeon Eevee=>Umbreon

VAPOREON™
Bubble Jet Pokémon

PRONUNCIATION: vay-POR-ey-on
TYPE: Water
HEIGHT: 1.0m   WEIGHT: 29kg
ATTACKS: Tackle, Sand-Attack
STRONG AGAINST: Fire, Ground, Rock
WEAK AGAINST: Water, Grass, Dragon
EVOLUTION: Eevee =>Vaporeon

JOLTEON™
Lightning Pokémon

PRONUNCIATION: JOLT-e-on
TYPE: Electric
HEIGHT: 0.8m   WEIGHT: 24.5kg
ATTACKS: Tackle, Sand-Attack
STRONG AGAINST: Water, Flying
WEAK AGAINST: Electric, Grass, Dragon
EVOLUTION: Eevee =>Jolteon

FLAREON™
Flame Pokémon

PRONUNCIATION: FLARE-ae-on
TYPE: Fire
HEIGHT: 0.9m   WEIGHT: 25kg
ATTACKS: Tackle, Sand-Attack
STRONG AGAINST: Grass, Ice, Bug, Steel
WEAK AGAINST: Fire, Water, Rock, Dragon
EVOLUTION: Eevee =>Flareon

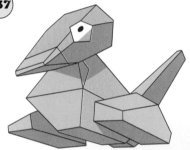

PORYGON™
Virtual Pokémon

PRONUNCIATION: POR-eh-gon
TYPE: Normal
HEIGHT: 0.8m   WEIGHT: 36.5kg
ATTACKS: Tackle, Conversion
STRONG AGAINST: None
WEAK AGAINST: Rock, Steel
EVOLUTION: Porygon=>Porygon2

OMANYTE™
Spiral Pokémon

PRONUNCIATION: AHM-uh-nite
TYPE: Rock/Water
HEIGHT: 0.4m   WEIGHT: 7.5kg
ATTACKS: Water Gun, Withdraw
STRONG AGAINST: Fire, Ice, Flying, Bug, Rock, Ground
WEAK AGAINST: Fighting, Ground, Steel, Water, Grass, Dragon
EVOLUTION: Omanyte=>Omastar

OMASTAR™
Spiral Pokémon

PRONUNCIATION: AHM-uh-star
TYPE: Rock/Water
HEIGHT: 1.0m   WEIGHT: 35kg
ATTACKS: Water Gun, Withdraw, Spike Cannon
STRONG AGAINST: Fire, Ice, Flying, Bug, Rock, Ground
WEAK AGAINST: Fighting, Ground, Steel, Water, Grass, Dragon
EVOLUTION: Omanyte=>Omastar

KABUTO™
Shellfish Pokémon

PRONUNCIATION: kuh BOO-toe
TYPE: Rock/Water
HEIGHT: 0.5m   WEIGHT: 11.5kg
ATTACKS: Scratch, Harden
STRONG AGAINST: Fire, Ice, Flying, Bug, Rock, Ground
WEAK AGAINST: Fighting, Ground, Steel, Water, Grass, Dragon
EVOLUTION: Kabuto=>Kabutops

KABUTOPS™
Shellfish Pokémon

PRONUNCIATION: kuh-BOO-tops
TYPE: Rock/Water
HEIGHT: 1.3m   WEIGHT: 40.5kg
ATTACKS: Scratch, Harden, Absorb, Slash
STRONG AGAINST: Fire, Ice, Flying, Bug, Rock, Ground
WEAK AGAINST: Fighting, Ground, Steel, Water, Grass, Dragon
EVOLUTION: Kabuto=>Kabutops

AERODACTYL™
Fossil Pokémon

PRONUNCIATION: AIR-oh-dack-tull
TYPE: Rock/Flying
HEIGHT: 1.8m   WEIGHT: 59kg
ATTACKS: Wing Attack, Agility
STRONG AGAINST: Fire, Ice, Flying, Bug, Grass, Fighting
WEAK AGAINST: Fighting, Ground, Steel, Electric, Rock
EVOLUTION: None

SNORLAX™
Sleeping Pokémon

PRONUNCIATION:	SNORE-lacks
TYPE:	Normal
HEIGHT:	2.1m WEIGHT: 460kg
ATTACKS:	Headbutt, Amnesia, Rest
STRONG AGAINST:	None
WEAK AGAINST:	Rock, Steel
EVOLUTION:	None

ARTICUNO™
Freeze Pokémon

PRONUNCIATION:	ARE-ti-koo-no
TYPE:	Ice/Flying
HEIGHT:	1.7m WEIGHT: 55.4kg
ATTACKS:	Ice Beam
STRONG AGAINST:	Grass, Ground, Flying, Dragon, Fighting, Bug
WEAK AGAINST:	Fire, Water, Ice, Steel, Electric, Rock
EVOLUTION:	None

ZAPDOS™
Electric Pokémon

PRONUNCIATION:	ZAP-dose
TYPE:	Electric/Flying
HEIGHT:	1.6m WEIGHT: 52.6kg
ATTACKS:	Thundershock, Drill Peck
STRONG AGAINST:	Water, Flying, Grass, Fighting, Bug
WEAK AGAINST:	Electric, Grass, Dragon, Rock
EVOLUTION:	None

MOLTRES™
Flame Pokémon

PRONUNCIATION:	Mole-trace
TYPE:	Fire/Flying
HEIGHT:	2.0m WEIGHT: 60kg
ATTACKS:	Fire Spin
STRONG AGAINST:	Grass, Ice, Bug, Steel, Fighting
WEAK AGAINST:	Fire, Water, Rock, Dragon, Electric
EVOLUTION:	None

DRATINI™
Dragon Pokémon

PRONUNCIATION:	druh-TEE-nee
TYPE:	Dragon
HEIGHT:	1.8m WEIGHT: 3.3kg
ATTACKS:	Wrap, Leer
STRONG AGAINST:	Dragon
WEAK AGAINST:	Steel
EVOLUTION:	Dratini=>Dragonair=> Dragonite

DRAGONAIR™
Dragon Pokémon

PRONUNCIATION:	DRAG-uh-nair
TYPE:	Dragon
HEIGHT:	4.0m WEIGHT: 16.5kg
ATTACKS:	Wrap, Leer, Thunder wave
STRONG AGAINST:	Dragon
WEAK AGAINST:	Steel
EVOLUTION:	Dratini=>Dragonair=> Dragonite

DRAGONITE™
Dragon Pokémon

PRONUNCIATION:	DRAG-uh-nite
TYPE:	Dragon/Flying
HEIGHT:	2.2m WEIGHT: 210kg
ATTACKS:	Wrap, Leer, Thunder wave, Agility, Slam, Dragon Rage
STRONG AGAINST:	Dragon, Grass, Fighting, Bug
WEAK AGAINST:	Steel, Electric, Rock
EVOLUTION:	Dratini=>Dragonair=> Dragonite

MEWTWO™
Genetic Pokémon

PRONUNCIATION:	MYU -too
TYPE:	Psychic
HEIGHT:	2.0m WEIGHT: 122kg
ATTACKS:	Confusion, Disable, Swift
STRONG AGAINST:	Fighting, Poison
WEAK AGAINST:	Psychic, Steel
EVOLUTION:	None

CHIKORITA™
Leaf Pokémon

PRONUNCIATION:	CHICK-or-eeee-tuh
TYPE:	Grass
HEIGHT:	0.9m WEIGHT: 6.4kg
ATTACKS:	Tackle, Growl, Razor Leaf
STRONG AGAINST:	Water, Ground, Rock
WEAK AGAINST:	Fire, Grass, Poison, Flying, Bug, Dragon, Steel
EVOLUTION:	Chikorita=>Bayleef=> Meganium

BAYLEEF™
Leaf Pokémon

PRONUNCIATION: Bay Leef
TYPE: Grass
HEIGHT: 1.2m WEIGHT: 15.8kg
ATTACKS: Razor Leaf, Reflect, Poisonpowder, Synthesis
STRONG AGAINST: Water, Ground, Rock
WEAK AGAINST: Fire, Grass, Poison, Flying, Bug, Dragon, Steel
EVOLUTION: Chikorita=>Bayleef=> Meganium

MEGANIUM™
Herb Pokémon

PRONUNCIATION: Muh-gay-knee-lam
TYPE: Grass
HEIGHT: 1.8m WEIGHT: 100.5kg
ATTACKS: Synthesis, Body Slam, Light Screen, Safeguard
STRONG AGAINST: Water, Ground, Rock
WEAK AGAINST: Fire, Grass, Poison, Flying, Bug, Dragon, Steel
EVOLUTION: Chikorita=>Bayleef=> Meganium

CYNDAQUIL™
Fire Mouse Pokémon

PRONUNCIATION: Sin-da-qwil
TYPE: Fire
HEIGHT: 0.5m WEIGHT: 7.9kg
ATTACKS: Tackle, Leer, Smokescreen, Ember
STRONG AGAINST: Grass, Ice, Bug, Steel
WEAK AGAINST: Fire, Water, Rock, Dragon
EVOLUTION: Cyndaquil=>Quilava=> Typhlosion

QUILAVA™
Volcano Pokémon

PRONUNCIATION: Qwi-lava
TYPE: Fire
HEIGHT: 0.9m WEIGHT: 19kg
ATTACKS: Ember, Quick Attack, Flame Wheel
STRONG AGAINST: Grass, Ice, Bug, Steel
WEAK AGAINST: Fire, Water, Rock, Dragon
EVOLUTION: Cyndaquil=>Quilava=> Typhlosion

TYPHLOSION™
Volcano Pokémon

PRONUNCIATION: Tie-flow-sion
TYPE: Fire
HEIGHT: 1.7m WEIGHT: 79.5kg
ATTACKS: Flame Wheel, Swift, Flamethrower
STRONG AGAINST: Grass, Ice, Bug, Steel
WEAK AGAINST: Fire, Water, Rock, Dragon
EVOLUTION: Cyndaquil=>Quilava=> Typhlosion

TOTODILE™
Big Jaw Pokémon

PRONUNCIATION: Tot-o-dile
TYPE: Water
HEIGHT: 0.6m WEIGHT: 9.5kg
ATTACKS: Scratch, Leer, Range, Water Gun
STRONG AGAINST: Fire, Ground, Rock
WEAK AGAINST: Water, Grass, Dragon
EVOLUTION: Totodile=>Croconaw=> Feraligatr

CROCONAW™
Big Jaw Pokémon

PRONUNCIATION: CROC-o-naw
TYPE: Water
HEIGHT: 1.1m WEIGHT: 25kg
ATTACKS: Rage, Water Gun, Bite, Scary Face
STRONG AGAINST: Fire, Ground, Rock
WEAK AGAINST: Water, Grass, Dragon
EVOLUTION: Totodile=>Croconaw=> Feraligatr

FERALIGATR™
Big Jaw Pokémon

PRONUNCIATION: FUR-al-i-gay-ler
TYPE: Water
HEIGHT: 2.3m WEIGHT: 88.8kg
ATTACKS: Bite, Scary Face, Slash, Screech, Hydro Pump
STRONG AGAINST: Fire, Ground, Rock
WEAK AGAINST: Water, Grass, Dragon
EVOLUTION: Totodile=>Croconaw=> Feraligatr

SENTRET™
Scout Pokémon

PRONUNCIATION: SEN-trit
TYPE: Normal
HEIGHT: 0.8m WEIGHT: 6kg
ATTACKS: Tackle, Defence Curl, Quick Attack
STRONG AGAINST: None
WEAK AGAINST: Rock, Steel
EVOLUTION: Sentret=>Furret

162

FURRET™
Long Body Pokémon

TYPE:	Normal
HEIGHT:	1.8m **WEIGHT:** 32.5kg
ATTACKS:	Fury Swipes, Slam, Rest, Amnesia
STRONG AGAINST:	None
WEAK AGAINST:	Rock, Steel
EVOLUTION:	Sentret=>Furret

163

HOOTHOOT™
Owl Pokémon

PRONUNCIATION:	HOOT-Hoot
TYPE:	Normal/Flying
HEIGHT:	0.7m **WEIGHT:** 21.2kg
ATTACKS:	Tackle, Growl, Foresight, Peck
STRONG AGAINST:	Grass, Fighting, Bug
WEAK AGAINST:	Rock, Steel, Electric
EVOLUTION:	Hoothoot=>Noctowl

164

NOCTOWL™
Owl Pokémon

TYPE:	Normal/Flying
HEIGHT:	1.6m **WEIGHT:** 40.8kg
ATTACKS:	Reflect, Take Down, Confusion
STRONG AGAINST:	Grass, Fighting, Bug
WEAK AGAINST:	Rock, Steel, Electric
EVOLUTION:	Hoothoot=>Noctowl

165

LEDYBA™
Five Star Pokémon

PRONUNCIATION:	LAY-dee-bah
TYPE:	Bug/Flying
HEIGHT:	1.0m **WEIGHT:** 10.8kg
ATTACKS:	Tackle, Supersonic, Comet Punch
STRONG AGAINST:	Grass, Psychic, Dark, Fighting, Bug
WEAK AGAINST:	Fire, Fighting, Flying, Ghost, Steel, Electric, Rock
EVOLUTION:	Ledyba=>Ledian

166

LEDIAN™
Five Star Pokémon

TYPE:	Bug/Flying
HEIGHT:	1.4m **WEIGHT:** 35.6kg
ATTACKS:	Light Screen, Baton Pass, Comet Punch, Swift,
STRONG AGAINST:	Grass, Psychic, Dark, Fighting, Bug
WEAK AGAINST:	Fire, Fighting, Flying, Ghost, Steel, Electric, Rock
EVOLUTION:	Ledyba=>Ledian

167

SPINARAK™
String Spit Pokémon

PRONUNCIATION:	SPIN-a-rack
TYPE:	Bug/Poison
HEIGHT:	0.5m **WEIGHT:** 8.5kg
ATTACKS:	Poison Sting, String Shot, Scary Face, Constrict
STRONG AGAINST:	Grass, Water, Ground, Rock
WEAK AGAINST:	Grass, Bug, Fire, Fighting, Flying, Poison, Ground, Rock, Ghost, Dark, Dragon, Steel
EVOLUTION:	Spinarak=>Ariados

168

ARIADOS™
Long Leg Pokémon

TYPE:	Bug/Poison
HEIGHT:	1.1m **WEIGHT:** 33.5kg
ATTACKS:	Leech Life, Fury Swipes, Spider Web, Screech
STRONG AGAINST:	Grass, Water, Ground, Rock
WEAK AGAINST:	Grass, Bug, Fire, Fighting, Flying, Poison, Ground, Rock, Ghost, Dark, Dragon, Steel
EVOLUTION:	Spinarak=>Ariados

170

CHINCHOU™
Angler Pokémon

TYPE:	Water/Electric
HEIGHT:	0.5m **WEIGHT:** 12kg
ATTACKS:	Bubble, Thunder Wave, Flail, Water Gun, Spark
STRONG AGAINST:	Fire, Ground, Rock, Water, Flying
WEAK AGAINST:	Water, Grass, Dragon, Electric, Dragon
EVOLUTION:	Chinchou=>Lanturn

171

LANTURN™
Light Pokémon

TYPE:	Water/Electric
HEIGHT:	1.2m **WEIGHT:** 22.5kg
ATTACKS:	Spark, Confuse Ray, Take Down, Hydro Pump
STRONG AGAINST:	Fire, Ground, Rock, Water, Flying
WEAK AGAINST:	Water, Grass, Dragon, Electric, Dragon
EVOLUTION:	Chinchou=>Lanturn

172

PICHU™
Tiny Mouse Pokémon

TYPE: Electric
HEIGHT: 0.3m   WEIGHT: 2kg
ATTACKS: Thundershock, Charm, Tail Whip, Thunder Wave
STRONG AGAINST: Water, Flying
WEAK AGAINST: Electric, Grass, Dragon
EVOLUTION: Pichu=>Pikachu=>Raichu

173

CLEFFA™
Starshape Pokémon

PRONUNCIATION: CLEFF-ah
TYPE: Normal
HEIGHT: 0.3m   WEIGHT: 3kg
ATTACKS: Pound, Charm, Encore, Sing, Sweet Kiss
STRONG AGAINST: None
WEAK AGAINST: Rock, Steel
EVOLUTION: Cleffa=>Clefairy=> Clefable

174

IGGLYBUFF™
Balloon Pokémon

PRONUNCIATION: IGG-lee-buff
TYPE: Normal
HEIGHT: 0.3m   WEIGHT: 1kg
ATTACKS: Sing, Charm, Defense Curl, Pound, Sweet Kiss
STRONG AGAINST: None
WEAK AGAINST: Rock, steel
EVOLUTION: Igglybuff=>Jigglypuff=> Wigglytuff

175

TOGEPI™
Spike Ball Pokémon

PRONUNCIATION: TOE-gah-pee
TYPE: Normal
HEIGHT: 0.3m   WEIGHT: 1.5kg
ATTACKS: Charm, Metronome, Sweet Kiss, Encore
STRONG AGAINST: None
WEAK AGAINST: Rock, Steel
EVOLUTION: Togepi=>Togetic

176

TOGETIC™
Happiness Pokémon

PRONUNCIATION:
TYPE: Normal/Flying
HEIGHT: 0.6m   WEIGHT: 3.2kg
ATTACKS: Encore, Safeguard, Double-Edge
STRONG AGAINST: Grass, Fighting, Bug
WEAK AGAINST: Rock, Steel, Electric
EVOLUTION: Togepi=>Togetic

177

NATU™
Little Bird Pokémon

TYPE: Psychic/Flying
HEIGHT: 0.2m   WEIGHT: 2kg
ATTACKS: Peck, Leer, Night Shade, Teleport
STRONG AGAINST: Fighting, Poison, Grass, Bug
WEAK AGAINST: Psychic, Steel, Electric, Rock
EVOLUTION: Natu=>Xatu

178

XATU™
Mystic Pokémon

TYPE: Psychic/Flying
HEIGHT: 1.5m   WEIGHT: 15kg
ATTACKS: Future Sight, Confuse Ray, Psychic
STRONG AGAINST: Fighting, Poison, Grass, Bug
WEAK AGAINST: Psychic, Steel, Electric, Rock
EVOLUTION: Natu=>Xatu

179

MAREEP™
Wool Pokémon

PRONUNCIATION: Ma-reep
TYPE: Electric
HEIGHT: 0.6m   WEIGHT: 7.8kg
ATTACKS: Tackle, Growl, Thundershock
STRONG AGAINST: Water, Flying
WEAK AGAINST: Electric, Grass, Dragon
EVOLUTION: Mareep=>Flaaffy=> Ampharos

180

FLAAFFY™
Wool Pokémon

TYPE: Electric
HEIGHT: 0.8m   WEIGHT: 13.3kg
ATTACKS: Thunder Wave, Cotton Spore
STRONG AGAINST: Water, Flying
WEAK AGAINST: Electric, Grass, Dragon
EVOLUTION: Mareep=>Flaaffy=> Ampharos

181 AMPHAROS™
Light Pokémon

TYPE:	Electric
HEIGHT:	1.4m **WEIGHT:** 61.5kg
ATTACKS:	Light Screen, Thunder
STRONG AGAINST:	Water, Flying
WEAK AGAINST:	Electric, Grass, Dragon
EVOLUTION:	Mareep=>Flaaffy=> Ampharos

182 BELLOSSOM™
Flower Pokémon

PRONUNCIATION:	BELL-aew-sum
TYPE:	Grass
HEIGHT:	0.4m **WEIGHT:** 5.8kg
ATTACKS:	Absorb, Sweet Scent, Stun Spore, Petal Dance
STRONG AGAINST:	Water, Ground, Rock
WEAK AGAINST:	Fire, Grass, Poison, Flying, Bug, Dragon, Steel
EVOLUTION:	Oddish=>Gloom=>Bellosom

183 MARILL™
Aquamouse Pokémon

PRONUNCIATION:	MARE-ill
TYPE:	Water
HEIGHT:	0.4m **WEIGHT:** 8.5kg
ATTACKS:	Tackle, Defence Curl, Tail Whip, Water Gun, Rollout
STRONG AGAINST:	Fire, Ground, Rock
WEAK AGAINST:	Water, Grass, Dragon
EVOLUTION:	Marill=>Azumarill

184 AZUMARILL™
Aquarabbit Pokémon

TYPE:	Water
HEIGHT:	0.8m **WEIGHT:** 28.5kg
ATTACKS:	Bubble Beam, Submission, Rain Dance
STRONG AGAINST:	Fire, Ground, Rock
WEAK AGAINST:	Water, Grass, Dragon
EVOLUTION:	Marill=>Azumarill

185 SUDOWOODO™
Imitation Pokémon

PRONUNCIATION:	
TYPE:	Rock
HEIGHT:	1.2m **WEIGHT:** 38kg
ATTACKS:	Rock Throw, Mimic, Flail, Low Kick, Rock Slide, Slam
STRONG AGAINST:	Fire, Ice, Flying, Bug
WEAK AGAINST:	Fighting, Ground, Steel
EVOLUTION:	None

187 HOPPIP™
Cottonweed Pokémon

PRONUNCIATION:	HOP-pip
TYPE:	Grass/Flying
HEIGHT:	0.4m **WEIGHT:** 0.5kg
ATTACKS:	Splash, Synthesis, Tail Whip, Tackle, Stun Spore
STRONG AGAINST:	Water, Ground, Rock, Grass, Fighting, Bug
WEAK AGAINST:	Fire, Grass, Poison, Flying, Bug, Dragon, Steel, Electric, Rock
EVOLUTION:	Hoppip=>Skiploom=> Jumpluff

188 SKIPLOOM™
Cottonweed Pokémon

TYPE:	Grass/Flying
HEIGHT:	0.6m **WEIGHT:** 1kg
ATTACKS:	Poisonpowder, Stun Spore, Sleep Powder
STRONG AGAINST:	Water, Ground, Rock, Grass, Fighting, Bug
WEAK AGAINST:	Fire, Grass, Poison, Flying, Bug, Dragon, Steel, Electric, Rock
EVOLUTION:	Hoppip=>Skiploom=> Jumpluff

189 JUMPLUFF™
Cottonweed Pokémon

TYPE:	Grass/Flying
HEIGHT:	0.8m **WEIGHT:** 3kg
ATTACKS:	Stun Spore, Sleep Powder, Leech Seed, Cotton Spore
STRONG AGAINST:	Water, Ground, Rock, Grass, Fighting, Bug
WEAK AGAINST:	Fire, Grass, Poison, Flying, Bug, Dragon, Steel, Electric, Rock
EVOLUTION:	Hoppip=>Skiploom=> Jumpluff

190 AIPOM™
Long Tail Pokémon

TYPE:	Normal
HEIGHT:	0.8m **WEIGHT:** 11.5kg
ATTACKS:	Sand-Attack, Baton Pass, Fury Swipes, Swift, Agility
STRONG AGAINST:	None
WEAK AGAINST:	Rock, Steel
EVOLUTION:	None

191

SUNKERN™
Seed Pokémon

TYPE:	Grass
HEIGHT:	0.3m **WEIGHT:** 1.8kg
ATTACKS:	Absorb, Growth, Mega Drain, Sunny Day
STRONG AGAINST:	Water, Ground, Rock
WEAK AGAINST:	Fire, Grass, Poison, Flying, Bug, Dragon, Steel
EVOLUTION:	Sunkern=>Sunflora

192

SUNFLORA™
Sun Pokémon

TYPE:	Grass
HEIGHT:	0.8m **WEIGHT:** 8.5kg
ATTACKS:	Pound, Razor Leaf, Sunny Day, Petal Dance
STRONG AGAINST:	Water, Ground, Rock
WEAK AGAINST:	Fire, Grass, Poison, Flying, Bug, Dragon, Steel
EVOLUTION:	Sunkern=>Sunflora

193

YANMA™
Clear Wing Pokémon

TYPE:	Bug/Flying
HEIGHT:	1.2m **WEIGHT:** 38kg
ATTACKS:	Foresight, Quick Attack, Double Team, Sonicboom
STRONG AGAINST:	Grass, Psychic, Dark, Fighting, Bug
WEAK AGAINST:	Fire, Fighting, Flying, Ghost, Steel, Electric, Rock
EVOLUTION:	None

194

WOOPER™
Water Fish Pokémon

TYPE:	Water/Ground
HEIGHT:	0.4m **WEIGHT:** 8.5kg
ATTACKS:	Water Gun, Tail Whip, Slam, Amnesia
STRONG AGAINST:	Fire, Ground, Rock, Fire, Electric, Poison, Rock, Steel
WEAK AGAINST:	Water, Grass, Dragon, Bug
EVOLUTION:	Wooper=>Quagsire

195

QUAGSIRE™
Water Fish Pokémon

TYPE:	Water/Ground
HEIGHT:	1.4m **WEIGHT:** 75kg
ATTACKS:	Earthquake, Rain Dance, Mist, Haze
STRONG AGAINST:	Fire, Ground, Rock, Fire, Electric, Poison, Rock, Steel
WEAK AGAINST:	Water, Grass, Dragon, Bug
EVOLUTION:	Wooper=>Quagsire

198

MURKROW™
Darkness Pokémon

TYPE:	Dark/Flying
HEIGHT:	0.5m **WEIGHT:** 2.1kg
ATTACKS:	Peck, Pursuit, Haze, Night Shade, Faint Attack
STRONG AGAINST:	Psychic, Ghost, Grass, Fighting, Bug
WEAK AGAINST:	Fighting, Dark, Steel, Electric, Rock
EVOLUTION:	None

199

SLOWKING™
Royal Pokémon

PRONUNCIATION:	SLOW-king
TYPE:	Water/Psychic
HEIGHT:	2.0m **WEIGHT:** 79.5kg
ATTACKS:	Curse, Water Gun, Confusion, Disable
STRONG AGAINST:	Fire, Ground, Rock, Fighting, Poison
WEAK AGAINST:	Water, Grass, Dragon, Psychic, Steel
EVOLUTION:	Slowpoke=>Slowking

201

UNOWN™
Symbol Pokémon

TYPE:	Psychic/Hidden Power
HEIGHT:	0.5m **WEIGHT:** 5kg
ATTACKS:	Hidden Power
STRONG AGAINST:	Fighting, Poison
WEAK AGAINST:	Pyschic, Steel
EVOLUTION:	None

202

WOBBUFFET™
Patient Pokémon

PRONUNCIATION:	
TYPE:	Psychic
HEIGHT:	1.3m **WEIGHT:** 28.5kg
ATTACKS:	Counter, Mirror Coat, Destiny Bond
STRONG AGAINST:	Fighting, Poison
WEAK AGAINST:	Psychic, Steel
EVOLUTION:	None

203

GIRAFARIG™
Long Neck Pokémon

TYPE:	Normal/Psychic
HEIGHT:	1.5m **WEIGHT:** 41.5kg
ATTACKS:	Confusion, Stomp, Agility, Psybeam
STRONG AGAINST:	Fighting, Poison
WEAK AGAINST:	Rock, Steel, Psychic
EVOLUTION:	None

204

PINECO™
Bagworm Pokémon

TYPE:	Bug
HEIGHT:	0.6m **WEIGHT:** 7.2kg
ATTACKS:	Selfdestruct, Take Down, Rapid Spin, Bide
STRONG AGAINST:	Grass, Psychic, Dark
WEAK AGAINST:	Fire, Fighting, Flying, Ghost, Dark
EVOLUTION:	Pineco=>Forretress

207

GLIGAR™
Flyscorpio Pokémon

PRONUNCIATION:	GLIE-gar
TYPE:	Ground/Flying
HEIGHT:	1.1m **WEIGHT:** 64.8kg
ATTACKS:	Poison Sting, Sand-Attack, Slash
STRONG AGAINST:	Fire, Electric, Poison, Rock, Steel, Grass, Fighting, Bug
WEAK AGAINST:	Grass, Bug, Electric, Rock
EVOLUTION:	None

208

STEELIX™
Iron Snake Pokémon

TYPE:	Steel/Ground
HEIGHT:	9.2m **WEIGHT:** 400kg
ATTACKS:	Bind, Rock Throw, Rage, Sandstorm, Slam, Bite
STRONG AGAINST:	Ice, Bug, Fire, Electric, Poison, Rock, Steel
WEAK AGAINST:	Fire, Water, Grass, Bug
EVOLUTION:	Onix=>Steelix

209

SNUBBULL™
Fairy Pokémon

PRONUNCIATION:	SNUB-bul
TYPE:	Normal
HEIGHT:	0.6m **WEIGHT:** 7.8kg
ATTACKS:	Scary Face, Tail Whip, Charm, Bite, Lick, Roar
STRONG AGAINST:	None
WEAK AGAINST:	Rock, Steel
EVOLUTION:	Snubbull=>Granbull

210

GRANBULL™
Fairy Pokémon

TYPE:	Normal
HEIGHT:	1.4m **WEIGHT:** 48.7kg
ATTACKS:	Bite, Lick, Roar, Rage, Take Down
STRONG AGAINST:	None
WEAK AGAINST:	Rock, Steel
EVOLUTION:	Snubbull=>Granbull

213

SHUCKLE™
Mold Pokémon

TYPE:	Bug/Rock
HEIGHT:	0.6m **WEIGHT:** 20.5kg
ATTACKS:	Constrict, Withdraw, Wrap, Encore, Bide
STRONG AGAINST:	Grass, Psychic, Dark, Fire, Ice, Flying, Bug
WEAK AGAINST:	Fire, Fighting, Flying, Ghost, Steel, Ground
EVOLUTION:	None

214

HERACROSS™
Single Horn Pokémon

PRONUNCIATION:	HAIR-a-cross
TYPE:	Bug/Fighting
HEIGHT:	1.5m **WEIGHT:** 54kg
ATTACKS:	Horn Attack, Endure, Fury Attack, Counter, Take Down.
STRONG AGAINST:	Grass, Psychic, Dark, Normal, Ice, Rock, Steel
WEAK AGAINST:	Fire, Fighting, Flying, Ghost, Steel, Poison, Psychic, Bug
EVOLUTION:	None

216

TEDDIURSA™
Little Bear Pokémon

TYPE:	Normal
HEIGHT:	0.6m **WEIGHT:** 8.8kg
ATTACKS:	Lick, Fury Swipes, Faint Attack, Rest
STRONG AGAINST:	None
WEAK AGAINST:	Rock, Steel
EVOLUTION:	Teddiursa=>Ursaring

217

URSARING™
Hibernate Pokémon

PRONUNCIATION:
TYPE:	Normal
HEIGHT:	1.8m WEIGHT: 125.8kg
ATTACKS:	Slash, Snore, Thrash
STRONG AGAINST:	None
WEAK AGAINST:	Rock, Steel
EVOLUTION:	Teddiursa=>Ursaring

220

SWINUB™
Pig Pokémon

TYPE:	Ice/Ground
HEIGHT:	0.4m WEIGHT: 6.5kg
ATTACKS:	Tackle, Powder Snow, Endure, Take Down
STRONG AGAINST:	Grass, Ground, Flying, Dragon, Fire, Electric, Poison, Rock, Steel
WEAK AGAINST:	Fire, Water, Ice, Steel, Grass, Bug
EVOLUTION:	Swinub=>Piloswine

221

PILOSWINE™
Swine Pokémon

TYPE:	Ice/Ground
HEIGHT:	1.1m WEIGHT: 55.8kg
ATTACKS:	Fury Attack, Mist, Blizzard
STRONG AGAINST:	Grass, Ground, Flying, Dragon, Fire, Electric, Poison, Rock, Steel
WEAK AGAINST:	Fire, Water, Ice, Steel, Grass, Bug
EVOLUTION:	Swinub=>Piloswine

226

MANTINE™
Kite Pokémon

TYPE:	Water/Flying
HEIGHT:	2.1m WEIGHT: 220kg
ATTACKS:	Bubble, Supersonic, Bubble Beam, Take Down
STRONG AGAINST:	Fire, Ground, Rock, Grass, Fighting, Bug
WEAK AGAINST:	Water, Grass, Dragon, Electric, Rock
EVOLUTION:	None

231

PHANPY™
Long Nose Pokémon

TYPE:	Ground
HEIGHT:	0.5m WEIGHT: 33.5kg
ATTACKS:	Tackle, Growl, Defense Curl, Flail, Take Down
STRONG AGAINST:	Fire, Electric, Poison, Rock, Steel
WEAK AGAINST:	Grass, Bug
EVOLUTION:	Phanpy=>Donphan

232

DONPHAN™
Armour Pokémon

PRONUNCIATION:	DON-fan
TYPE:	Ground
HEIGHT:	1.1m WEIGHT: 120kg
ATTACKS:	Rollout, Earthquake, Rapid Spin
STRONG AGAINST:	Fire, Electric, Poison, Rock, Steel
WEAK AGAINST:	Grass, Bug
EVOLUTION:	Phanpy=>Donphan

234

STANTLER™
Big Horn Pokémon

PRONUNCIATION:	STANT-ler
TYPE:	Normal
HEIGHT:	1.4m WEIGHT: 71.2kg
ATTACKS:	Hypnosis, Stomp, Sand-Attack, Confuse Ray
STRONG AGAINST:	None
WEAK AGAINST:	Rock, Steel
EVOLUTION:	None

235

SMEARGLE™
Painter Pokémon

TYPE:	Normal
HEIGHT:	1.2m WEIGHT: 58kg
ATTACKS:	Sketch
STRONG AGAINST:	None
WEAK AGAINST:	Rock, Steel
EVOLUTION:	None

237

HITMONTOP™
Handstand Pokémon

TYPE:	Fighting
HEIGHT:	1.4m WEIGHT: 48kg
ATTACKS:	Rolling Kick
STRONG AGAINST:	Normal, Ice, Rock, Dark, Steel
WEAK AGAINST:	Poison, Flying, Psychic, Bug
EVOLUTION:	Tyrogue=>Hitmontop

239

ELEKID™
Electric Pokémon

PRONUNCIATION:	EL-ah-kid
TYPE:	Electric
HEIGHT:	0.6m WEIGHT: 23.5kg
ATTACKS:	Thunder Punch, Light Screen, Thunder Bolt
STRONG AGAINST:	Water, Flying
WEAK AGAINST:	Electric, Grass, Dragon
EVOLUTION:	Elekid=>Electabuzz

241

MILTANK™
Milk Cow Pokémon

TYPE:	Normal
HEIGHT:	1.2m WEIGHT: 75.5kg
ATTACKS:	Stomp, Bide, Rollout, Body Slam
STRONG AGAINST:	None
WEAK AGAINST:	Rock, Steel
EVOLUTION:	None

242

BLISSEY™
Happiness Pokémon

PRONUNCIATION:	
TYPE:	Normal
HEIGHT:	1.5m WEIGHT: 46.8kg
ATTACKS:	Pound, Doubleslap, Sing, Egg Bomb, Light Screen
STRONG AGAINST:	None
WEAK AGAINST:	Rock, Steel
EVOLUTION:	Chansey=>Blissey

244

ENTEI™
Volcano Pokémon

TYPE:	Fire
HEIGHT:	2.1m WEIGHT: 198kg
ATTACKS:	Ember, Roar, Fire Spin, Stomp, Flamethrower
STRONG AGAINST:	Grass, Ice, Bug, Steel
WEAK AGAINST:	Fire, Water, Rock, Dragon
EVOLUTION:	None

249

LUGIA™
Diving Pokémon

PRONUNCIATION:	LU-gee-ah
TYPE:	Psychic/Flying
HEIGHT:	5.2m WEIGHT: 216kg
ATTACKS:	Aeroblast, Gust, Hydro Pump, Rain Dance
STRONG AGAINST:	Fighting, Poison, Grass, Bug
WEAK AGAINST:	Psychic, Steel, Electric, Rock, Steel
EVOLUTION:	None

250

HO-OH™
Rainbow Pokémon

PRONUNCIATION:	HO-Ho
TYPE:	Fire/Flying
HEIGHT:	3.8m WEIGHT: 199kg
ATTACKS:	Sacred Fire, Fire Blast, Sunny Day
STRONG AGAINST:	Ice, Steel, Grass, Bug, Fighting
WEAK AGAINST:	Fire, Water, Rock, Dragon, Steel, Electric, Rock
EVOLUTION:	None

TEAM ROCKET

To protect the world from devastation.
To unite all peoples within our nation.
To denounce the evils of truth and love.
To extend our reach to the stars above.
Jessie
James
Team Rocket blast off at the speed of light.
Surrender now or prepare to fight.
Me-e-owth that's right!

POKÉMON SEARCH

It's all in the shadows!

Can you identify all the Pokémon shadows on these pages? They are all listed below to help you.

HOUNDOUR
SNORLAX MAGBY
DUNSPARCE DODUO
ODDISH MAGCARGO
AERODACTYL
PORYGON2 MILTANK
VULPIX OCTILLERY
EEVEE STANTLER
RATTATA GIRAFARIG
PIKACHU ESPEON

1 Epseon

2 Howndour

3 Snorlax

4 Rattata

5 Girafarig

6

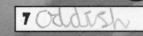

7 Oddish

8 Doudo

9 [_____]

10 [_____]

11 [_____]

12 [_____]

13 Vulpix

14 Pickachu

15 octillery

16 evel

17 Stanler

18 Magby

93

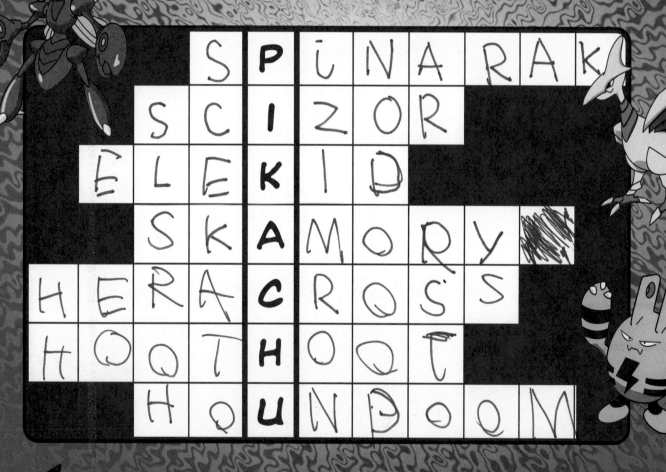

Pokémon WORD PUZZLE

Grid Match

We have placed Ash's Pokémon friend Pikachu into the grid. Can you match the names below to the other Pokémon shown here and write them in the grid?

HERACROSS • HOUNDOOM

SCIZOR • HOOTHOOT

ELEKID • SPINARAK

SKAMORY

BYE, BYE, BUTTERFREE

One sunny day, as Ash, Pikachu, Misty and Brock made their way to a new city and a new gym, they paused at a cliff ledge to look out at the sea.
"Hey, what are those?" asked Ash, pointing up at the sky.
"They look like Butterfree!" said Misty.
"This is the season when Butterfree find mates," said Brock. "Then they fly across the sea to lay their eggs."
Ash gulped and said, "You mean my Butterfree would go, too?"
If you don't let it cross the sea, it will never have babies," Brock replied.

Ash and his friends decided to rent a hot air balloon to get close to the Butterfree, as many other Butterfree trainers were doing. Soon the friends were quickly floating in the air, going higher and higher!

"Hold on, guys!" said Brock.
"Wow!" said Ash. "What a view!"
"Look!" said Misty. "All the Butterfree are pairing off!"
"Any time now, Ash," hinted Brock.

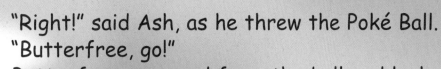

"Right!" said Ash, as he threw the Poké Ball.
"Butterfree, go!"
Butterfree emerged from the ball and looked at
Ash curiously.
"Go out there and find your mate!" coaxed Ash.
"Good luck, Butterfree!" called Misty.

As Ash and his friends held their breath, Butterfree looked around at all the other Butterfree.

Then it finally flew over to one that was still by itself.

"Butterfree found someone it likes!" said Ash happily. "Yeah, it's love at first sight with that pink one," said Brock. Butterfree fluttered and danced around the pink Butterfree.

But the pink Butterfree wanted nothing to do with poor Butterfree.
"Butterfree!" called Ash.
"Have confidence in yourself! Show it your Whirlwind Attack!"
Butterfree showed off its strength,
but the pink Butterfree was still not
impressed.
"Pika, Pika," said Pikachu sadly.
As they all wondered how to help
Butterfree, they noticed a helicopter
speeding toward the Butterfree swarm.

It had a big red R on the door. Ash
realised that the helicopter belonged to ...
TEAM ROCKET!
Out from the bottom of the helicopter came a giant net. It began to
scoop up hundreds of Butterfree!

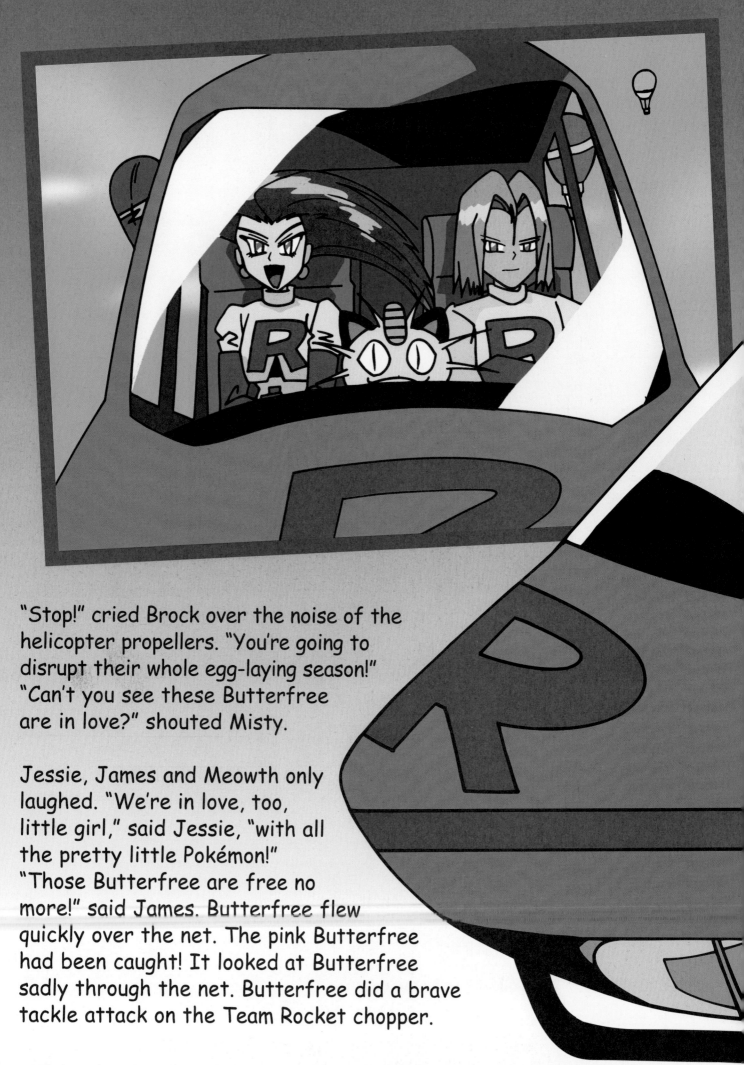

"Stop!" cried Brock over the noise of the helicopter propellers. "You're going to disrupt their whole egg-laying season!" "Can't you see these Butterfree are in love?" shouted Misty.

Jessie, James and Meowth only laughed. "We're in love, too, little girl," said Jessie, "with all the pretty little Pokémon!" "Those Butterfree are free no more!" said James. Butterfree flew quickly over the net. The pink Butterfree had been caught! It looked at Butterfree sadly through the net. Butterfree did a brave tackle attack on the Team Rocket chopper.

"That pathetic little insect thinks it can stop us," said Jessie.
"Butterfree, Stun Spore now!" called Ash.
Butterfree flew above the helicopter and tried to shower down its Stun Spore – but the revolving blades just blew it away from the chopper. Team Rocket turned and headed in another direction. They were getting away! Butterfree followed the chopper as fast as it could.

Eventually, Ash and his friends found Butterfree waiting for them. Butterfree led them down to a deep canyon where, in a warehouse, Team Rocket had hidden their stolen Butterfree.

"What a great catch!" said James as he looked at the net stuffed with Butterfree.
Just then, Team Rocket heard some glass breaking.
"Hey – somebody's bustin' in!" cried Meowth.

"Who is it? Who's there?" cried Jessie.
Ash and his friends broke through the window!
"Prepare for trouble!" announced Ash.
"And you can make that triple!" added Misty.
"We're defending the beauty of truth and love!"

"Butterfree, go!" cried Ash, hurling the
Poké Ball.
"Starmie, tackle attack!" ordered Misty.
And the battle for the Butterfree began.
As the pink Butterfree watched hopefully,
Butterfree attacked the net again and again. But

it wasn't able to tear it. Finally, summoning all its strength, Butterfree hit it one more time – and tore a big hole through the net!

The Butterfree were free at last!

"Take this!" cried Jessie, swinging at Starmie.
But Misty easily revived Starmie with water, and soon
Starmie was ready to battle.

Meanwhile, Brock opened
the door of the
warehouse.
"Hurry up! Fly away!" he
cried, as the Butterfree quickly
escaped.
Team Rocket was determined to get
back the Butterfree. They managed to
get back into their helicopter – and it didn't take them long to catch
up to the Butterfree swarm.
Ash, Pikachu, Misty and Brock rushed back to their hot air balloon
and took off in the air after Team Rocket.

Now it was Pikachu's turn to help the Butterfree. Pikachu hopped on Butterfree's back and together they flew over to the Team Rocket helicopter.

Brave little Pikachu jumped off Butterfree's back and landed on the chopper.
Team Rocket gasped in fear.
"It's going to shock us! It's going to shock us!" they cried.
With Pikachu's powerful Thundershock Attack, Team Rocket was soon blasting off again!

Now the pink Butterfree was dancing for Butterfree! "All right!" said Ash. "Good for you, Butterfree!" But inside, Ash felt sad. He knew that it was now time for Butterfree to leave him and fly across the ocean with the pink Butterfree.

Ash knelt down to talk to Butterfree, who was also feeling sad. "Don't worry, Butterfree," said Ash softly. "I'll just tell all the other Pokémon that you're on a trip – and that you'll come back someday. Good-bye, Butterfree." As the two Butterfree took off into the sky, Ash

thought about all the wonderful times he'd had with Butterfree, as they'd travelled from town to town.

"Good-bye, Butterfree!" I'll always remember you – thank you for everything!" called Ash, as the Butterfree disappeared into the sunset.

Brock put his hand on Ash's shoulder. "Ash, you raised Butterfree to have a lot of courage," he said. "And I think you just proved that you have lots of courage, too."

Good friendships last forever, even though friends don't always stay together. Helping Butterfree to grow, Ash just may have also grown himself!